Scholastic Success With
2nd GRADE
WORKBOOK

SCHOLASTIC

NEW YORK • TORONTO • LONDON • AUCKLAND • SYDNEY
MEXICO CITY • NEW DELHI • HONG KONG • BUENOS AIRES

Cover design by Anna Christian; Cover art by Rob McClurkan

Interior illustrations by Jon Buller, Reggie Holladay, Anne Kennedy, Bob Masheris, Mark Mason, Marybeth Rivera, and Carol Tiernon
Interior design by Quack & Company
Maps (pages 209–254) copyright © 2002 Linda Ward Beech

Photos ©: 113: Yayasya/iStockphoto; 257 top: Kiki Dohmeier/Shutterstock; 257 bottom: Bill Curtsinger/National Geographic Creative; 257 bottom inset: Edie Widder/Visuals Unlimited, Inc.; 262 top: IgorKovalchuk/Thinkstock; 262 bottom: GlobalP/Thinkstock; 264 left: VanessaVolk/Thinkstock; 264 right: Vac1/Thinkstock; 269 top: Geng Xu/Thinkstock; 269 bottom: Algul/Thinkstock; 274 top: Ola Lundqvist/Shutterstock; 274 center: Dirk Ercken/Shutterstock; 274 bottom: Jeffrey B. Banke/Shutterstock; 276: Richard Mackson/Getty Images; 279 top: pmphoto/iStockphoto; 279 center top: Tymofii85/iStockphoto; 279 center bottom: Rodney_X/iStockphoto; 279 bottom: vaeenma/iStockphoto; 282 left: bergamont/iStockphoto; 282 right: szefei/iStockphoto; 282 bottom: leah613/iStockphoto; 285 top: badmanproduction/iStockphoto; 285 center top: Photo Researchers, Inc./Science Source; 285 center bottom: Richard Weymouth Brooks/Science Source; 285 bottom: BrankoBG/iStockphoto; 286 center: Medioimages/Photodisc/Thinkstock; 286 inset: Beautiful landscape/Shutterstock; 287 top left: badmanproduction/iStockphoto; 287 top right: Richard Weymouth Brooks/Science Source; 287 bottom left: Photo Researchers, Inc./Science Source; 287 bottom right: BrankoBG/iStockphoto; 288 top: Orla/iStockphoto; 288 left: takenobu/Thinkstock; 288 bottom: Niclasbo/iStockphoto; 291: YinYang/iStockphoto; 293: Tagstock1/iStockphoto; 295 left: etiennevoss/iStockphoto; 295 right: ferlistockphoto/iStockphoto; 295 bottom: Gangis_Khan/iStockphoto; 298: Eraxion/Thinkstock; 386: Yuri Samsonov/Shutterstock.

ISBN 978-1-338-30659-0

Table of Contents

READING COMPREHENSION

CONTEMPORARY MANUSCRIPT

MAPS

SCIENCE

ADDITION & SUBTRACTION

"Nothing succeeds like success."

Alexandre Dumas the Elder, 1854

Dear Parent,

Congratulations on choosing this excellent educational resource for your child. Scholastic has long been a leader in educational publishing—creating quality educational materials for use in school and at home for nearly a century.

As a partner in your child's academic success, you'll want to get the most out of the learning experience offered in this book. To help your child learn at home, try following these helpful hints:

★ Provide a comfortable place to work.

★ Have frequent work sessions, but keep them short.

★ Praise your child's successes and encourage his or her efforts. Offer positive help when your child makes a mistake.

★ Display your child's work and share his or her progress with family and friends.

In this workbook you'll find hundreds of practice pages that keep kids challenged and excited as they strengthen their skills across the classroom curriculum.

The workbook is divided into eight sections: Reading Comprehension; Contemporary Manuscript; Grammar; Writing; Maps; Science; Addition & Subtraction; and Math. You and your child should feel free to move through the pages in any way you wish.

The table of contents lists the activities and the skills practiced. And a complete answer key in the back will help you gauge your child's progress.

Take the lead and help your child succeed with the *Scholastic Success With 2nd Grade Workbook!*

FOCUS SKILLS

The activities in this workbook reinforce age-appropriate skills and will help your child meet the following standards established as goals by leading educators.

Mathematics

★ Uses a variety of strategies when problem-solving

★ Understands and applies number concepts

★ Uses basic and advanced procedures while performing computation

★ Understands and applies concepts of measurement

★ Understands and applies concepts of geometry

Writing

★ Understands and uses the writing process

★ Uses grammatical and mechanical conventions in written compositions

Reading

★ Understands and uses the general skills and strategies of the reading process

★ Can read and understand a variety of literary texts

★ Can understand and interpret a variety of informational texts

Geography

★ Understands the characteristics and uses of maps and globes

★ Knows the location of places, geographic features, and patterns of the environment

Science

★ Plans and carries out investigations to answer questions or test solutions

★ Examines animals, insects, and plants and how they interact with their environment

★ Identifies the basic physical structure of insects, plants, and humans

★ Analyzes processes that shape the earth

★ Recognizes and interprets weather patterns

★ Understands the relationship between sound and vibration

Scholastic Success With

READING COMPREHENSION

Try This!

*When you are reading, do you get stuck on words that you don't know? Does not knowing a word make it hard to understand what you are reading? This idea can help you. Use **context clues** to figure out what the word is. That means think about the other words in the sentence. What clues do they give? Then ask yourself what other word would make sense there.*

What do you think the underlined word means in each sentence below? Circle the meaning that makes sense. Then rewrite each sentence using the meaning instead of the underlined word.

1. **My domino has two white <u>pips</u>, and yours has five.**

   baby dogs   spots   long metal tubes

   _____

2. **A gray <u>fulmar</u> flew by the cruise ship.**

   lizard   swordfish   seabird

   _____

3. **The queen had a beautiful necklace made of <u>jasper</u>.**

   a green stone   yellow pudding   wet snow

   _____

4. **My sister is the best <u>flutist</u> in the high school band.**

   waitress   runner   flute player

   _____

 Write a meaning for this nonsense word: zeebit. Use it in a sentence on another piece of paper. See if a friend can guess the meaning of your word by looking at the clues in the sentence.

© Scholastic Inc.

Moon Walk

 *The **main idea** tells what the whole story is about.*

Neil Armstrong was an astronaut. He made history on July 20, 1969. He was the first man to walk on the moon! When he stepped on the moon, he said, "That's one small step for (a) man, one giant leap for mankind." Millions of people were watching this amazing event on TV. It was an awesome thing to look up at the moon that night and know that a man was walking around on it! For years, people had wondered if there would be moon creatures living there. But the only things Armstrong found were moon rocks and moon dust.

Draw a line connecting the correct star words that tell the main idea of the story. Begin at Earth. Some star words will not be used.

uncle ☆　　dance ☆　　　　　　　walk ☆　　moon ⬤

　　　　　　　　　to ☆

river ☆　　　　　　　　　　　on ☆

　　　cold ☆　　　uncle ☆

Armstrong ☆　　　　　　　　　　the ☆

　　was ☆　　man ☆

　　　　　　　　　　　frog ☆

Neil 🌍　　　　hat ☆

　　the ☆　　　　　　candy ☆

　　　　　　　　plate ☆

　　first ☆

💡 **Write a short story with this title: "My Trip to the Moon."**
Underline the main idea of the story.

ABC

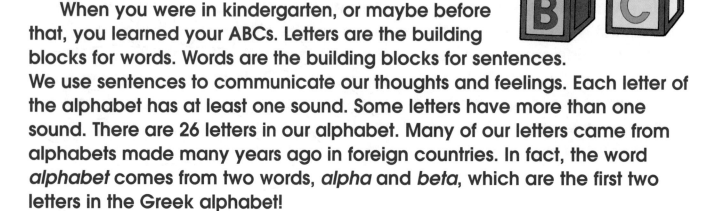

*The **main idea** of a story tells what the whole story is about.*

When you were in kindergarten, or maybe before that, you learned your ABCs. Letters are the building blocks for words. Words are the building blocks for sentences. We use sentences to communicate our thoughts and feelings. Each letter of the alphabet has at least one sound. Some letters have more than one sound. There are 26 letters in our alphabet. Many of our letters came from alphabets made many years ago in foreign countries. In fact, the word *alphabet* comes from two words, *alpha* and *beta*, which are the first two letters in the Greek alphabet!

Underline the title that describes the main idea of this story.

Playing With Blocks   **All About Our Alphabet**   **The Greek Language**

Now let's play a game using the alphabet. Read each clue below. Draw a line to the letters that sound like the correct answer.

1. I borrowed some money from your piggy bank. _____ fifty cents.

2. This math is not hard. It's _____.

3. What did the blind man say to the doctor who made him see again? _____

4. What insect makes honey? _____

5. What might a Native American sleep in? _____

6. I drank all my milk. Now my glass is _____.

7. What kind of plant is that? _____

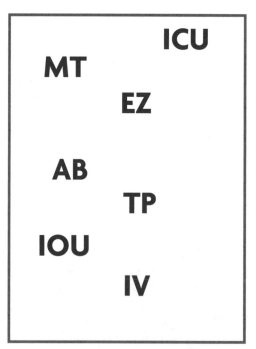

ICU

MT

EZ

AB

TP

IOU

IV

Call the Police!

It is good to know that you can call a police officer when you need help. You should not be afraid of the police. Their job is to help people. Police officers help find lost children. They direct traffic when there is a problem on the roads. They arrest criminals so that our towns are safe. When people have been in car accidents, police officers come quickly to help them. During floods, fires, and tornadoes, they take people to safe places. Sometimes they rescue people who are in danger. Police officers have saved many lives. Think of a police officer as your best friend!

What do you think the main idea of this story is? To find out, read the letters that are connected in the puzzle. Write the letters in order beside the matching shapes.

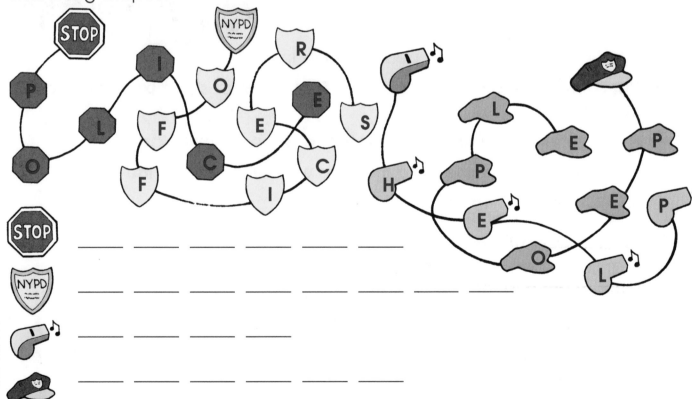

 Write a letter to your town's police officers. Make sure the letter's main idea is to thank them for keeping your town safe. Ask an adult to mail it for you.

Rachel's Recipe

Details *are parts of a story. Details help you understand what the story is about.*

On Saturday, Rachel got up early. Her mom was still asleep, so Rachel made her own breakfast. She put some peanut butter in a bowl. She mixed it with a little honey. Then she stirred in some oatmeal, bran flakes, and raisins. It tasted yummy! When Mom got up, she said, "Oh! You made granola!"

Follow the directions below.

- Circle the word that tells who the main character is.

- Underline the word that tells what day Rachel made breakfast.

- Put a box around the word that tells what dish Rachel put the peanut butter in.

- Put a star by each of the four words that tell what she mixed with the peanut butter.

- Put a dotted line under the word that describes how it tasted.

- Put two lines under the word that tells what Mom called the food.

Now find each of the nine words in the puzzle below and circle it. The words go across and down.

```
B R A N F L A K E S M H N C L
O A T M E A L B K E Q O J W I
W R A I S I N S G R A N O L A
L G S A T U R D A Y P E R D R
G R A C H E L Y U M M Y F A H
```

On another sheet of paper, draw your favorite breakfast. Then write the steps to prepare it.

Rodeo Clowns

Details *are parts of a story. Details help you understand what the story is about.*

Have you ever been to a rodeo or seen one on TV? If so, you probably saw some rodeo clowns. Like clowns at a circus, they entertain the audience by doing funny tricks to make people laugh. But the main job of rodeo clowns is to protect the cowboys from the bulls. They try to catch the bull's attention long enough to allow the cowboy to escape from the arena without getting hurt. Bulls are quite fast, and they make sudden moves, so it is hard to get away from them. Angry bulls use their horns as weapons. Rodeo clowns sometimes jump in a barrel while the bull pushes it around. Other times they wave their arms or yell to keep the bull away from the cowboy. They make it look like a funny game, but it is really a very dangerous job.

Circle the letter under true or false to show your answer.

True	False	
B	Z	1. Rodeo clowns do funny tricks.
R	U	2. Rodeo clowns work at the circus.
L	M	3. Rodeo clowns help protect the cowboys.
A	L	4. Rodeo clowns distract the goats while the cowboy gets away.
R	X	5. Rodeo clowns are brave.
I	V	6. Bulls can make sudden moves.
F	D	7. Bulls use their tails as weapons.
P	E	8. Sometimes rodeo clowns jump in a cardboard box while the bull pushes it around.
R	W	9. Sometimes rodeo clowns yell and wave their arms to distract the bulls.
S	C	10. Rodeo clowns have a very dangerous job.

To find out who likes rodeo clowns, write the letters you circled in order.

___ ___ ___ ___ ___ ___ ___ ___ ___ ___

Gorillas

b 0 0d0

➤ **Details** *are parts of a story. Details help you understand what the story is about.*

Gorillas are the largest apes. They live in the rain forests of Africa. Every morning, they wake up and eat a breakfast of leaves, fruit, and bark. During most of the day, the adult gorillas take naps. Meanwhile, young gorillas play. They wrestle and chase each other. They swing on vines. When the adults wake up, everyone eats again. When there is danger, gorillas stand up on their hind legs, scream, and beat their chests. Every night before it gets dark, the gorillas build a new nest to sleep in. They break off leafy branches to make their beds, either on the ground or in the trees. Baby gorillas snuggle up to their mothers to sleep.

Find the answers to the puzzle in the story. Write the answers in the squares with the matching numbers.

Across
1. During the day, adult gorillas _____. *nap*
3. Gorillas eat leaves, bark, and _____. *fruit*
5. The largest apes are _____. *gorillas*
7. In danger, gorillas beat their _____. *chests*
8. Young gorillas swing on _____. *vines*

Down
2. The continent where gorillas live is _____. *Africa*
4. When young gorillas play, they _____ and chase each other. *wrestle*
6. Baby gorillas snuggle up to their mothers to _____. *sleep*

On another piece of paper, write two things gorillas do that people also do.

Fun at the Farm

 Story events that can really happen are **real**. *Story events that are make-believe are* **fantasy**.

Read each sentence below. If it could be real, circle the picture.
If it is make-believe, put an X on the picture.

 Dairy cows give milk.

 The farmer planted pizza and hamburgers.

 The pig said, "Let's go to the dance tonight!"

 The mouse ate the dinner table.

 The hay was stacked in the barn.

 The chickens laid golden eggs.

 The green tractor ran out of gas.

 The newborn calf walked with wobbly legs.

 The goat and the sheep got married by the big tree.

 Two crickets sang "Mary Had a Little Lamb."

 Horses sat on the couch and watched TV.

 Rain made the roads muddy.

 Four little ducks swam in the pond.

 The farmer's wife baked a pumpkin pie.

 On another sheet of paper, write one make-believe sentence about the farmer's house and one real sentence about it.

Grandma Hugfuzzy

Grandma Hugfuzzy lived all alone in the country. She loved to sit on the porch and watch the animals. Every day, she put food out for the rabbits and raccoons. She fed the birds with scraps of bread. She put corn out for the deer. One terrible, awful, dreadful day, Grandma Hugfuzzy's house burned down. Poor Grandma! She had nowhere to go and no one to help her. She spent the night in an old barn on a bed of hay, crying herself to sleep. During the night, the animals came to her rescue. Nine black bears chopped down some trees. A herd of deer carried the wood on their antlers. Dozens of raccoons and squirrels worked all night building a log cabin for Grandma. Birds flew above the house nailing on the roof. When morning came, Grandma Hugfuzzy was amazed to see what her animal friends had done! She threw a big party for them that lasted ten years!

Write a red *R* on things that are real. Write a purple *F* on things that are fantasy.

a woman feeding animals

deer that carry lumber

a grandmother living alone

sleeping on hay in a barn

animals building a log cabin

Home Sweet Home

WELCOME

a house burning down

bears chopping down trees

birds that can nail on a roof

crying that her house burned

a party that lasted ten years

The first part of this story could be real. Draw a big orange star at the place where the story changes to fantasy.

The Change Game

Each sentence below is make-believe. Change it!
Rewrite the sentence so that it is real.
Study the example.

The broom carried the dog to the moon.

The broom was kept in the closet.

1. **The newborn baby was bigger than a house.**

   _____

2. **The walls were painted with gooey green slime.**

   _____

3. **The Queen of England turned into a frog.**

   _____

Now change and do it the other way! Each sentence below is real.
Change it so that it is fantasy. Study the example.

The moon is made of rocks and ice.

The moon is made of green cheese.

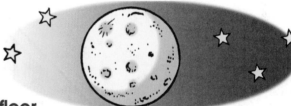

4. **The black spider crawled across the floor.**

   _____

5. **The deep-sea diver saw a whale and five dolphins.**

   _____

6. **My pizza has pepperoni and olives on it.**

   _____

 On another piece of paper, draw a picture about one of your fantasy sentences.

The Rescue

 Sequencing *means putting the events in a story in the order that they happened.*

Mia's black cat climbed to the top of a telephone pole and couldn't get down. "Come down, Spooky!" cried Mia. Mia thought hard. What could she do? She went across the street to ask Mr. Carson for help. He was a firefighter before he retired. "What's the matter, Mia?" asked Mr. Carson when he saw Mia's tears. "My cat is up on that pole, and I can't get her down!" Mr. Carson hugged Mia and said, "I'll call my buddies at the fire station. They will come and help." A few minutes later, Mia saw the fire truck coming. The firefighters parked near the pole and raised a long ladder to the top. A firefighter climbed the ladder and reached out for Spooky. Just then, Spooky jumped to a nearby tree limb, climbed down the tree, and ran into the backyard. Mia said, "Spooky! You naughty cat!" Mr. Carson and the firefighters laughed and laughed.

Read the sentences on the ladder. Number them in the order that they happen in the story.

Mia asked Mr. Carson for help.

Mr. Carson called his firefighter friends.

The firefighters laughed.

A firefighter climbed the ladder.

Mia begged Spooky to come down.

Spooky jumped to a tree and climbed down.

The fire truck came.

Mia scolded Spooky.

New Kid in School

When they finished moving, Mom took Shelby to meet her new teacher. The teacher said, "Welcome to our school, Shelby. Let me tell you what we do in our second-grade class. We start the day with reading and writing. After that, we do math. Then we go out to recess. Just before lunch, we have social studies. We eat lunch at 11:00. Then we have story time. After story time, we have science. Then comes learning centers, where you can work on the computer, play a game, or read a book. Next, we have spelling. Finally, we go to music and art classes for the last hour of the day. Here is a schedule for you to take home. I'll see you tomorrow, Shelby!"

Fill in the blanks with the missing words or time.

Second-Grade Class Schedule

Time	Activity
8:00	Reading and _____
9:00	_____
10:00	_____
10:30	_____
___:___	Lunch
11:30	_____
12:00	_____
1:00	Learning Centers
1:30	_____
2:00	_____ and Art
3:00	Go home.

A Pencil Sandwich?

How does the lead get inside a wooden pencil? Pencils are made out of strips of wood cut from cedar trees. Then grooves are cut in the strips. A mixture of graphite and clay is laid into the grooves. (We call it lead, but it is really a graphite mixture.) Then another strip of wood is glued on top of the first one, making a pencil sandwich! The wood is rounded in rows on the top strip of wood and the bottom strip. Then the pencils are cut apart and painted. An eraser is added on the end and held in place by a metal ring. When you buy a pencil, you sharpen it, and then you are ready to write.

Look at the pictures. Number them in the order that they happen in the story.

 Use a pencil to practice writing the alphabet, uppercase and lowercase.

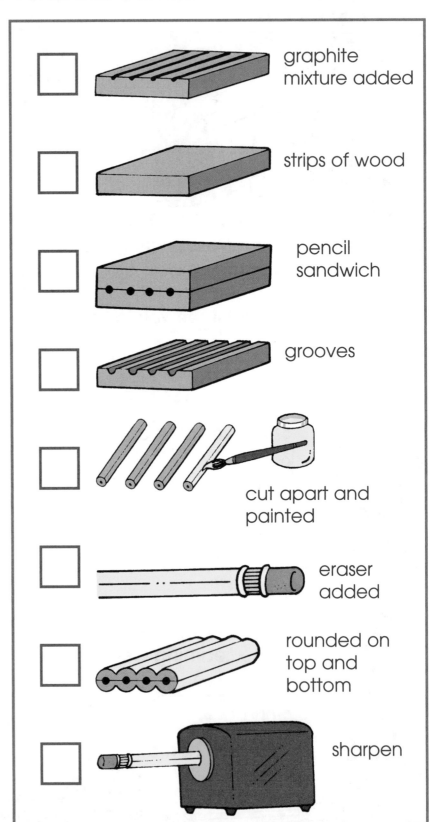

graphite mixture added

strips of wood

pencil sandwich

grooves

cut apart and painted

eraser added

rounded on top and bottom

sharpen

Secret Message

Follow the directions in each shape. Write the answer in the shape that matches it. If you follow directions carefully, you will discover a secret message!

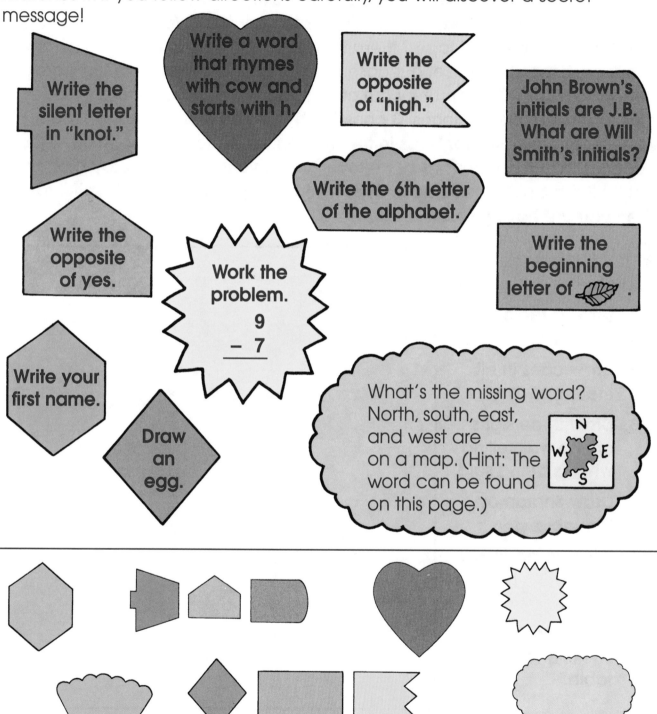

Write the silent letter in "knot."

Write a word that rhymes with cow and starts with h.

Write the opposite of "high."

John Brown's initials are J.B. What are Will Smith's initials?

Write the 6th letter of the alphabet.

Write the opposite of yes.

Write the beginning letter of 🍃 .

Write your first name.

Work the problem.
9
− 7

Draw an egg.

What's the missing word? North, south, east, and west are _____ on a map. (Hint: The word can be found on this page.)

 Write step-by-step directions that tell how to make a peanut butter and jelly sandwich.

Rainy Day Fun

One rainy afternoon, Sharon and I decided to play grocery store. We went to the garage and set up four empty boxes for our shelves. Mom let us have all the canned food from the pantry to play with. We wrote prices on little strips of paper and taped them to the cans. We used Dad's calculator for our cash register. We set our cash register on the old table in the garage. Then we got some play money out of a game in my closet. Sharon made signs that said, "Green Beans: 3 cans for $1.00" and things like that. There were lots of brown paper bags in the kitchen, so we took some to sack the groceries. When our cousins came over, we gave them some play money and let them be the customers. Then we traded places. Who cares if it rains when you are having so much fun?

Follow the directions to illustrate the story.

1. Draw a table and four empty boxes.

2. Draw cans in all the empty boxes.

3. Draw three signs on the wall telling what is being sold.

4. Draw Sharon by the table.

5. Draw some play money in Sharon's hand.

6. Draw two paper sacks under the table.

Write the directions from your house to a another place in your neighborhood. Follow the directions to see if they are correct.

Our Flag

I pledge allegiance to the flag of the United States of America and to the Republic for which it stands, one nation under God, indivisible, with liberty and justice for all.

Follow the directions given in each of the following sentences.

1. **There is one star for every state in the nation. Count the stars. Write the number in the star.**

2. **Write the name of your state.** _____

3. **Color the area around the stars blue. The stars should be white, so do not color them.**

4. **Write the total number of stripes.** _____

5. **Seven stripes are red. Beginning with the top stripe, color it and every other stripe red. The six stripes in between should be white, so do not color them.**

6. **Write these letters in reverse to make two words that tell another name for the flag.**   D   L   O   Y   R   O   L   G

   _____   _____

7. **Draw a box around every word in the Pledge of Allegiance that has more than six letters.**

Design a flag with four stars and three stripes for a make-believe country. Draw and color it.

After School at Jake's House

*You are **drawing conclusions** when you use your own thoughts to answer the question, "How could that have happened?"*

Jake had a lot of homework to do. It was three pages long. He added and subtracted until his hand got tired of writing.

1. What kind of homework did Jake have?

   spelling   math   reading

   What clues told you the answer? Underline them in the story.

After supper, Jake's dad reminded Jake to do his job. Jake went from room to room unloading baskets and cans into a large plastic bag. Then he took the bag out to the dumpster.

2. What was Jake's job?

   washing dishes   making the bed   taking out the trash

   What clues told you the answer? Underline them in the story.

Now Jake could have some free time. He decided to play "Star Monsters." He turned on the TV and put a cartridge in the player. He watched the monsters fighting on the TV screen while his fingers pushed buttons to make them move.

3. What was Jake doing?

   playing a video game   watching the news   playing with toys

   What clues told you the answer? Underline them in the story.

Jake was tired. He put on his pajamas, brushed his teeth, and crawled under the covers.

4. What was Jake doing?

   waking up   getting ready for school   going to bed

   What clues told you the answer? Underline them in the story.

© Scholastic Inc.

?ti si tahW

Friday was a special day at my school. First of all, we wore our clothes differently. The back pockets of my jeans were in the front, and my shirt was buttoned up in the back. The teacher began the day with the subject we usually did last. All day, our schedule was opposite of what it usually was. We had to write our name backwards on our papers. At lunch time, we ate dessert first, then our meals! When we went out to recess, we had to walk backward all the way to the playground. Then we had backward relay races. Some people fell down. Everyone was giggling! When it was time to go home, we sang "Good Morning to You."

1. **What special day was it? Circle one.**

    Valentine's Day   **Grandparent's Day**   **Backward Day**

2. **Connect the dots in backward ABC order to find out how the principal looked that day.**

3. **If the math assignment was to count by 5's to 50, how would the children have written it that day? Write the numbers.**

Make up a spelling word list with ten words. Then write them the way the children would have written them on this special day.

They Could Do Better

Read each story below. Choose your
answers from the bubble-gum machine.
Write them on the lines.

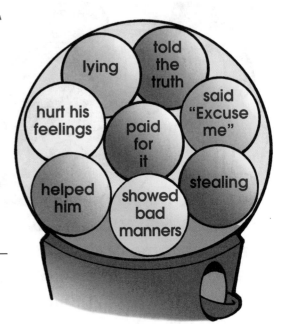

1. When no one was looking, James
   took a piece of bubble gum from
   the candy counter and chewed it.
   Then he left the store.

   What was James doing? _____

   What should he have done?

   _____

2. Dad's boss, Mr. Hill, came for dinner. Zach burped during
   the meal. He laughed. His dad looked angry.

   What did Zach do wrong? _____

   What should he have done? _____

3. Ashley went to her room to do her homework, but watched a video
   instead. When Mom came into her room, she asked, "Ashley, are you
   watching a video?" Ashley said, "No, Mom, I'm not."

   What was Ashley doing? _____

   What should she have done?_____

4. Becky and Cindy saw a boy trip and fall down. Becky pointed at him
   and told Cindy to look. Then they laughed. The boy looked away sadly.

   What did Becky and Cindy do? _____

   What should they have done?_____

 On a piece of paper, write the name of a person in your class who has good manners.
Explain why you came to that conclusion.

Miss Maple

I am a sugar tree. I live in Vermont. In the summer, my green leaves make a cool, shady place for people to rest. Every fall, my leaves turn brilliant colors of yellow, red, and orange. Some people think it looks like my leaves are on fire! In the winter, my leaves are all gone. I stretch my empty arms out to the falling snow. In the spring, little flowers appear along with my new leaves. That's when the sweet sap inside me begins to rise. People drill holes in my trunk and put a spout in me to drain the sap. Then they boil the sap and make maple syrup!

Add to and color each picture the way it is described in the story.

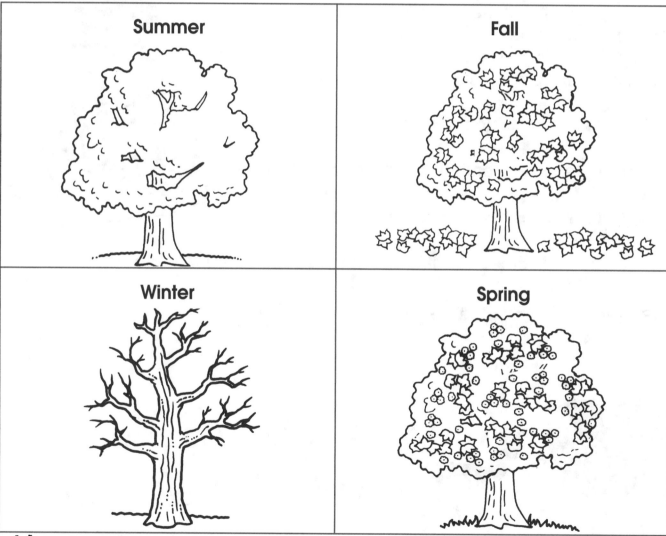

 Do you like maple syrup? Draw a picture of the kind of food that you would put maple syrup on.

Sentence Shapes

Let's have some fun reading and writing sentences! Look at the sentence below. It is shaped like what it is telling about.

I love rollercoasters. They are so much fun! They tickle my tummy!

Now it is your turn! Read each sentence below. Think about what it means. On another piece of paper, rewrite each sentence in the shape that shows what it is telling about. The shapes at the bottom of the page may help you.

1. I wonder if this box has my birthday gift in it.

2. I will send a valentine to someone that I love.

3. Columbus believed that Earth was round.

4. If you see someone without a smile, give them one of yours.

5. Jets taxi down the runway, then fly into the air.

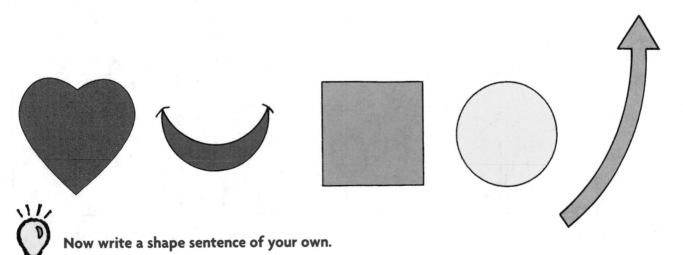

Now write a shape sentence of your own.

© Scholastic Inc.

Curious Creature

Use story details to help you make decisions about what has happened in the story.

Zolak boarded his spaceship and blasted off from the planet Vartog. He was on a special mission to learn about earthlings. His spaceship landed gently in a desert. Zolak walked around looking for earthlings, but all he could see were rocks and sand. Then he looked down and saw a dark creature lying down right next to him. In fact, the creature's feet were touching Zolak's feet. Zolak was scared and tried to run away, but everywhere he went, the creature followed him. At noon, Zolak realized that the creature had shrunk to a very small size but was still right next to his feet. However, during the afternoon, the dark creature grew longer and longer! Then the strangest thing happened. Night came and the dark creature completely disappeared!

1. Who do you think the dark creature was? _____

2. Was the dark creature an earthling?   yes   no

3. Do you think Zolak will give a true report about the earthlings when he returns to Vartog?   yes   no

   Why or why not?

   _____

4. Draw a line to match the object to its correct shadow.

 On a piece of paper, write the story you think will appear in Vartog newspapers under the headline "Zolak Discovers a Curious Creature on Earth?"

Figure It Out

Read each sentence. Then color the numbered space in the picture that matches the number of the correct answer.

He rode his bike?
Who rode it?
  1. a boy
  2. a girl

Please bait my hook.
What am I doing?
  7. fishing
  8. playing baseball

Sorry! I broke it.
What could it be?
  13. a stuffed animal
  14. a crystal vase

Look at the dark cloud.
Where should you look?
  19. down
  20. up

The lamb lost its mother.
Who is its mother?
  21. a sheep
  22. a horse

She wore a red hat.
Who wore it?
  23. a man
  24. a woman

I see a thousand stars.
What time is it?
  25. noon
  26. night

Let's throw snowballs!
What time of year is it?
  3. summer
  4. winter

Breakfast is ready!
What time is it?
  9. night
  10. morning

He's a professor.
What is he?
  15. an adult
  16. a baby

Run, John, run!
What sport is John in?
  5. swimming
  6. track

I'm so thirsty.
What will I do?
  11. drink something
  12. eat something

It won't fit in the car.
What is it?
  17. a football
  18. a swing set

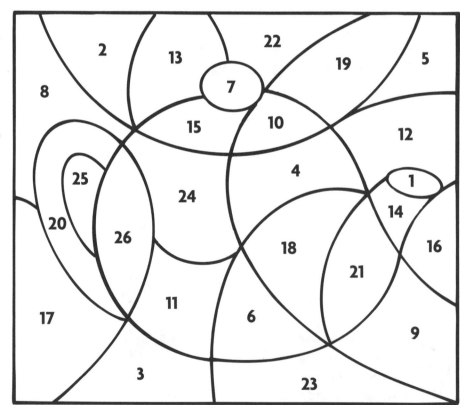

Riddle: What begins with T, ends with T, and has T in it? Find it in the puzzle.

© Scholastic Inc.

Summer Vacation

 Grouping like things together helps you see how parts of a story are connected and makes the story easier to understand.

Last summer, Dad, Mom, Tim, and Tara went to the beach in Florida. They swam, fished, built sandcastles, and went sailing. Mom brought a picnic lunch. She spread a blanket on the sand and set out ham sandwiches, potato chips, apples, and cookies. She brought lemonade in the cooler. Later, Tim and Tara walked along the beach and saw a crab walking sideways. A stray dog was barking at it. A starfish had washed up on the beach, too. Tim threw bread crumbs up in the air to feed a flock of seagulls. Then the family went back to the hotel, and Tim and Tara played video games until bedtime.

Use the story to find the answers. Fill in the blanks.

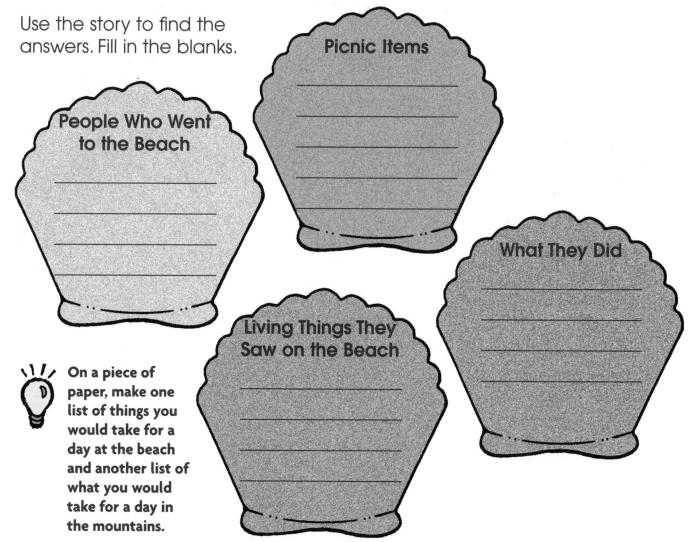

Picnic Items

People Who Went to the Beach

What They Did

Living Things They Saw on the Beach

On a piece of paper, make one list of things you would take for a day at the beach and another list of what you would take for a day in the mountains.

Which One Doesn't Belong?

 Look for similarities when grouping items.

Read each list. Cross out the word that doesn't belong. Then choose a word from the kite that belongs with each list and write it in the blank.

1. grouchy   mad   cheerful   fussy   _____

2. north   away   east   south   _____

3. goat   blue jay   robin   eagle   _____

4. juice   milk   tea   mud   _____

5. hand   toy   foot   head   _____

6. David   Bob   Ronald   Sarah   _____

7. spinach   cake   cookies   pie   _____

8. glue   bicycle   pencils   scissors   _____

9. penny   nickel   quarter   marble   _____

On the kite: arm, dime, George, pudding, lemonade, parakeet, crayons, angry, west

Now read these categories. In each box, write the number from the above list that matches the category.

Birds	Desserts	Bad Feelings
Boys' Names	Money	School Supplies
Directions	Body Parts	Drinks

 Write a list of five things that go with this category: **Things That Are Hot.**

My Favorites

This page is all about you! Read the categories and write your own answers.

My Favorite TV Shows	My Favorite Foods	My Favorite Sports
_____	_____	_____
_____	_____	_____
_____	_____	_____

Draw two of your favorite people here and write their names.

Favorite Thing to Do After School

_____

Favorite Thing to Do With My Family

_____

Favorite Color

ReD

_____

Favorite Holiday

_____

Favorite Song

_____

Favorite Movie

_____

Favorite School Subject

_____

Will He Be All Right?

Use story details to guess what will happen next.

Father Eagle said to his young son, "Today is a very special day. You will fly for the first time." Baby Eagle was afraid. He said, "But Father, I don't know how. What should I do?" His father laid a strong wing on his little shoulder and said, "You will know." They stood at the edge of a very high cliff. Far below were huge rocks and a canyon. "Ride the wind, my son!" said Father Eagle, and he gently pushed his son off the cliff. Baby Eagle yelled, "Help! Help!" and wildly flapped his wings. All of a sudden something wonderful happened!

Help!

He got hurt.

He fell on the rocks.

He broke his wing on a tree limb.

He learned to fly.

1. What do you think happened next? Color the rock that tells the most likely answer.

2. Why did you choose that answer? Find the sentence in the story that gives you a hint that the story has a happy ending. Write it here.

_____

_____

Unscramble the words and write the answer: **ODPRU**   **AARDFI**

3. How do you think Baby Eagle felt at first when he was pushed off the cliff? _____

4. How do you think Father Eagle felt at the end of the story? _____

What Will Happen Next?

Read each story. Write your answer on the blanks.

1. The baseball game was tied 6-6 at the bottom of the ninth inning with bases loaded. The home team batter hit a high fly ball deep into right field. The outfielder caught the ball but then dropped it. What will happen next?

_____

_____

_____

2. Latoya decided to bake some brownies. She put them in the oven and went outside and jumped in the pool. She swam for a long time. She forgot all about the brownies. What will happen next?

_____

_____

_____

3. Mrs. Lopez ran over a big nail. It stuck in the tire. Air began to seep out. What will happen next?

_____

_____

_____

4. The wind began to blow. Dark clouds drifted in. Lightning cracked, and thunder roared. What will happen next?

_____

_____

_____

5. One day Greg left his toy truck on the stairs. Mom came down the stairs carrying a laundry basket, piled high with dirty towels. She stepped on Greg's truck. What will happen next?

_____

_____

_____

6. Dad and Sam went fishing. They rowed the boat to the middle of the lake. Then they hit a rock that made a hole in the boat. Water started rushing in it. What will happen next?

_____

_____

_____

 Choose one of the stories above and draw a picture of what happens next.

Wishes Come True

Once upon a time Rita Rabbit was complaining to Diana Duck. "You always have fun, swimming around in the lake. I wish I was a duck. You're lucky." Diana Duck said, "Oh, really? Well, I wish I was a rabbit! You can hop so fast and go so far. I think you're lucky!" Just then the Good Fairy appeared and said, "You are both lucky! I will grant you each your wish." All of a sudden Rita Rabbit became a duck! She waddled to the lake and went for a swim. Diana Duck became a rabbit and hopped down the road as fast as she could go. At the end of the day, Rita was wet and cold. She missed her family. She missed her home in the hole at the bottom of the hollow tree. She wanted to hop over there, but it was too far, and all she could do was waddle. Diana was having trouble, too. She had hopped so far away that she got lost. She began to cry. She wanted to go home to the lake. Just then . . . POOF! The Good Fairy appeared again. She granted Rita and Diana one more wish.

Draw what you think happened when Rita got her second wish.

Draw what you think happened when Diana got her second wish.

 If you had a wish, what would it be? On a piece of paper, draw a picture of what might happen if your wish came true.

Zoo Reports

Compare *means to look for things that are the same.*
Contrast *means to look for things that are different.*

The second-grade class went to the zoo for a field trip. The next day, the teacher asked the children to write a report about what they learned. Read the two reports below.

Ryan

What I Learned at the Zoo

I learned about the giant tortoise. It was so big that the guide let us sit on its back. Some tortoises live to be over 100 years old! That's older than my grandpa!

The slowest-moving mammal is the three-toed sloth. It hangs from trees and eats leaves. Some sloths sleep more than 15 hours a day. What a lazy animal!

I thought the albino alligator was really cool. It wasn't green. It was completely white all over. It was born that way.

Jessica

What I Learned at the Zoo

The tallest animal on earth is the giraffe. It eats leaves from the tops of the trees. Giraffes come from Africa.

I learned about an albino alligator. It was white instead of green. The guide told us that it was born without the coloring of other alligators.

I saw an owl sleeping in a tree. Owls sleep in the daytime and hunt at night. When they sleep, they don't fall out of the tree because their claws lock onto the branch.

Ryan and Jessica each wrote about three animals. Write the names of the animals they wrote about in the correct circles. In the center where both circles overlap, write the name of the animal that they both wrote about.

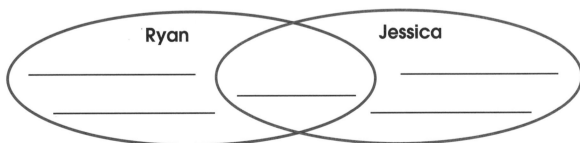

Write three facts about a zoo animal. If you need help, use a dictionary or encyclopedia.

The Contest

The Super Grocery Store held a contest. Whoever could guess the correct number of jelly beans in the big jar would win a prize. There were exactly 372 jelly beans. Two people guessed the right answer. They were Joey Jumpjolly and Harry Honkhorn. Since there were two winners, both of them were given a $20 gift certificate. Joey Jumpjolly decided to spend his prize money on his favorite foods. He bought vanilla ice cream, animal cookies, angel food cake, and a chocolate candy bar. Harry Honkhorn had a different idea. He used his money to buy bacon, eggs, cereal, and waffles.

How are Joey and Harry alike? How are they different? To find out, work the puzzle below. Cross out all the *Q*'s, *V*'s, *Z*'s, and *X*'s. Next cross out all the numbers 1–9. Then cross out every question mark. What is left? Write the words in order in the blanks at the bottom of the page.

3	?	5	Q	B	O	T	H	9	9	7	X	H	A	D	6	2
T	W	E	N	T	Y	X	Q	8	D	O	L	L	A	R	S	7
X	V	5	Z	T	O	4	?	Q	S	P	E	N	D	3	2	1
?	Q	J	O	E	Y	3	B	O	U	G	H	T	Z	V	7	6
Z	9	X	S	W	E	E	T	S	4	?	V	H	A	R	R	Y
7	?	V	Z	V	B	O	U	G	H	T	8	9	X	V	3	7
B	R	E	A	K	F	A	S	T	4	?	V	F	O	O	D	X

_____ _____ _____ _____

_____ _____. _____ _____

_____. _____

_____ _____.

On a piece of paper, make a list of what you would buy at a grocery store. Are your choices more like Joey's or Harry's?

The Accident

Kendra and her mom left their house on Oak Street to go to school. Kendra put on her safety belt. About that same time, Lacey and her mom left their house on Maple Street. On the way to school, Lacey bounced up and down on the seat watching her pigtails fly up and down in the mirror. She had forgotten to wear her safety belt. Both moms turned into the school parking lot at the same time, and they crashed into each other! Kendra was not hurt. Her safety belt kept her in her seat. But, Lacey fell forward and bumped her head HARD! She cried and cried. She had to go to the hospital and get an X ray. Lacey got well in a day or two, but she learned an important lesson!

Draw a 😊 in the correct column.

	Kendra	Lacey	both
driven to school by Mom			
wore a safety belt			
didn't wear a safety belt			
lives on Maple Street			
was in a wreck			
bumped her head			
got an X ray			
lives on Oak Street			
bounced up and down in the car			
didn't get hurt			
learned a lesson			

 Write a sentence telling why it is important to wear a safety belt.

What Is Cotton?

Cotton is a very useful plant. Farmers plant cotton in the spring. The plants grow and make white <u>flowers</u>. When a flower falls off, a <u>boll</u> grows in its place. The boll is the seed pod, which looks kind of like a walnut. When the boll dries, it splits open. Inside is the fluffy, white cotton. Farmers take the cotton to a <u>gin</u>. Machines at the gin take the cotton out of the bolls. The cotton is pressed into wrapped bundles called <u>bales</u>. The bales are sent to cotton mills where the cotton is spun into <u>yarn</u>. The yarn is woven into <u>fabric</u>, or cloth. Then it is made into clothes, sheets, curtains, towels, and many other things.

Draw a line from the word to its picture. The story will help you.

flowers •

boll •

gin •

• bales

• yarn

• fabric

Color the things below that could be made from cotton.
Put an X on things that are not made of cotton.

 Draw and color the clothes that you are wearing today. Put an X on the ones made of cotton.

Busy as a Bee

Bees are hardworking insects. They live together in a nest called a <u>hive</u>. There is one <u>queen bee</u> in each hive. She is the largest bee. There are hundreds of <u>worker bees</u>. The worker bees fly from flower to flower gathering a sweet liquid called <u>nectar</u>. They make honey from the nectar and store it in little rooms in the hive. Each little room is a <u>cell</u>. Many cells in a row make a <u>honeycomb</u>. When a bear or a person tries to steal the honey, the bees swarm, flying around in large groups. Each bee has a <u>stinger</u> to protect it from its enemies. A person who is a <u>beekeeper</u> makes wooden hives for bees, then sells the honey when the bees finish making it.

Look at the picture below. Use each underlined word in the story to label the pictures.

 On a piece of paper, make a list of five other insects. You may need an encyclopedia to help you.

Sioux Life

Many years ago, the Sioux people lived on the grasslands, called the <u>plains</u>. They killed bison for meat. Some called these animals <u>buffalo</u>. The Sioux cut the meat in strips and dried it in the sun to make <u>jerky</u>. Buffalo hides were used to make <u>tepees</u>. The hides were wrapped around long poles, making tall tents. The tepees could be taken down and moved around from place to place to follow the buffalo herds. <u>Canoes</u> were used for traveling down a river or crossing a lake. The Sioux made <u>buckskin clothing</u> out of deer hides. Sometimes they decorated their clothes with colorful beads. The leader was called the <u>chief</u>. The chief often wore a long <u>headdress</u> of eagle feathers.

Draw a line from each word to the picture that matches it.

- plains
- buffalo
- jerky
- tepee
- canoe
- buckskin clothing
- chief
- headdress

Circle the things below that the Sioux might have had.
Put an X on the things they didn't have.

Chain Reaction

*In a story, there is usually a reason something happens.
This is the **cause**. What happened as a result is the **effect**.*

It was a long way to Aunt Ruth's house. Terry and Mary Beth started getting a little bit too loud in the back seat, so Dad said, "Girls, settle down. Be quiet and read your books." They knew Dad meant business. Just then, Mary Beth saw a bee flying around in the car. Her eyes got big, and she ducked her head, swatting the bee away. Terry looked at her, and Mary Beth loudly whispered, "BEEEE!" Terry wanted to scream, but she knew Dad would get mad. "What are you two doing back there?" Dad asked. Just then, the bee landed on Dad's bald head. Mary Beth knew she had to save him from getting stung, so she whopped Dad on the head with her book. Dad jerked the steering wheel, and the car ran off the road and through a fence. The cows that were in the field ran away. Later, a police officer gave Dad a ticket for reckless driving.

Draw a line to match the cause to the effect.

The girls got too loud, so

The girls saw a bee land on Dad's bald head, so

The car ran off the road and through a fence

which let the cows out.

Dad said to be quiet.

Mary Beth whopped Dad on the head with a book.

Keep the chain going! Write what happened next because Dad got a ticket.

An American Volcano

Mount Saint Helens is an active volcano in the state of Washington. In 1980, this volcano erupted, spewing hot ash into the air. Eruptions caused a huge cloud of dust. This gray dust filled the air and settled on houses and cars many miles away. The thick dust made it hard for people and animals to breathe. The blast flattened trees on the side of the mountain. The hot ash caused forest fires. The snow that was on the mountain melted quickly, causing floods and mud slides. Mount Saint Helens still erupts from time to time but not as badly as it did in 1980.

Read each phrase below. Write the number of each phrase in the explosion of the volcano that correctly completes the sentence.

1. **Mount Saint Helens erupted,**

2. **The thick dust made it hard**

3. **The blast**

4. **The hot ash caused**

5. **Melting snow caused**

6. **Because Mount Saint Helens is an active volcano,**

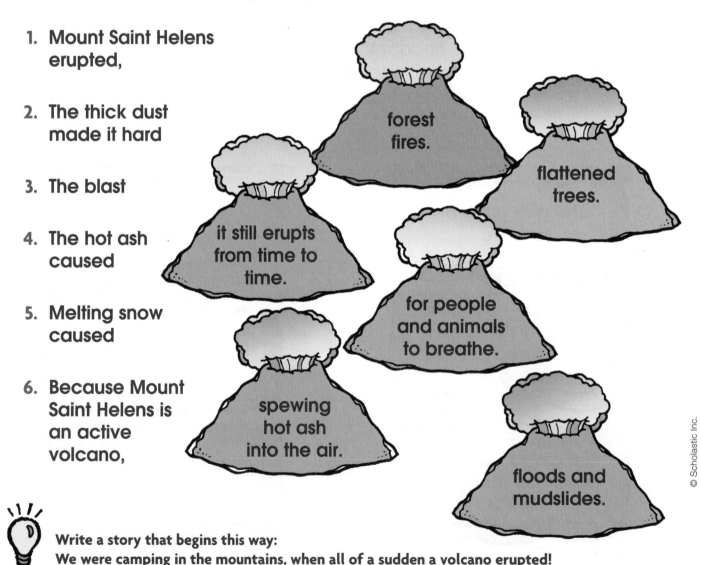

forest fires.

flattened trees.

it still erupts from time to time.

for people and animals to breathe.

spewing hot ash into the air.

floods and mudslides.

Write a story that begins this way:
We were camping in the mountains, when all of a sudden a volcano erupted!

My Favorite Dentist

 *A **character** is a person or animal in a story. To understand a character better, you should pay attention to the details a story often gives about the character.*

Some kids are scared to go to the dentist, but not me. I have a funny dentist. His name is Dr. Smileyface. I don't think that's his real name, but that's what he tells all the kids who come to see him. He has a cool waiting room. It has video games and a big toy box. Dr. Smileyface always wears funny hats. Sometimes he has his face painted. He asks funny questions. He makes me laugh.  One time, he told me this joke, "What has lots of teeth but never goes to the dentist? A comb!" When he pulled my tooth, it didn't hurt at all! He also teaches me how to take care of my teeth because he says he doesn't want me to get a cavity the size of the Grand Canyon. Before I go home, he always gives me a surprise. Last time I went, he gave me a rubber spider to scare my mom with!

Draw a line from the toothbrush to the ending that makes the sentence true.

1. Dr. Smileyface makes — how to take care of their teeth.

2. The child who wrote this story — with a surprise.

3. Dr. Smileyface teaches kids — his patients laugh.

4. Dr. Smileyface sends kids home — is not afraid to go to the dentist.

What a Kid!

Tad is a very special boy. He is confined to a wheelchair. He was born with a disease that made him unable to walk. Some boys would be sad or angry about that, but not Tad. Instead, he looks for ways to make people happy. He called the Green Oaks School for the Blind and asked if he could volunteer. They said, "Sure!" Tad went to the school and quickly made friends. Every day, he reads books to the children. He plays games with them. Sometimes he helps them do their schoolwork. The children at the school nicknamed him Lucky because they feel so lucky to have him as a friend. That makes Tad very happy!

- If Tad is confined to a wheelchair, write an H in Box 1 and Box 9. If not, write a J in both boxes.

- If Tad feels sorry for himself, write a U in Box 2 and Box 10. If he doesn't, write a E in both boxes.

- If Tad looks for ways to make people happy, write an L in Box 3. If he doesn't, write a B.

- If Tad volunteers at the River Oak School for the Blind, write a Z in Box 4. If that is not correct, write a P.

- If Tad reads to the blind children, write an N in Box 5. If not, write a V.

- If Tad plays games with the blind children, write a G in Box 6. If not, write a D.

- If Tad helps them with their homework, write an O in Box 7. If not, write an R.

- If the children nicknamed Tad "Grumpy," write a K in Box 8. If not, write a T.

- If Tad is a happy person, write an R in Box 11. If not, write a C.

This is the story of Helen Keller.

Tad's secret of happiness is

					I		

© Scholastic Inc.

The writing assignment in Ms. Daniels' class was to write about someone you admire. Read what one student wrote.

Lunch Lady

by Karen Jackson

I don't know her name. She is one of the workers in our school cafeteria. I just call her Lunch Lady. She's my friend. There are several nice ladies in the cafeteria, but the Lunch Lady is the nicest of all. Every day she smiles at me when I go through the line. She says things like, "Hi Karen! Are you having a good day?" Lunch Lady always remembers that I like chicken nuggets the best. Whenever that is what is being served, she hands me the chicken nuggets and says, "Look, your favorite!" One day, I tripped and dropped my tray. Food went all over the floor. I was so embarrassed, but Lunch Lady came to my rescue. She helped me pick up the mess, and she told me, "Don't worry about it. It's okay." That made me feel better. Another time, I was at the shoe store with my mom, and I saw Lunch Lady. She gave me a big hug. The reason I admire Lunch Lady is because she is friendly and kind.

Read each sentence. Find the words that are wrong and cross them out. Then above them write the correct word or words that make the sentence true.

1. Karen wrote about Lunch Man.

2. Karen's favorite food is hot dogs.

3. Lunch Lady frowns when Karen comes through the line.

4. When Karen dropped her tray, Miss Daniels helped her.

5. One time, Karen saw the Lunch Lady at the hardware store.

6. Karen admires Lunch Lady because she is friendly and mean.

 Write a paragraph about someone you admire.

Limericks

 A **limerick** *is a poem that has five lines in it. It is usually funny and has a special order of rhyming words. The first two lines rhyme. Then the next two lines rhyme. Then the last line rhymes with the first two lines. Read the limerick below.*

There once was a fellow named Jed

Who spent too much time in his bed.

He slept for so long

That something went wrong,

His hair grew long on his head.

In the limerick above, draw a red circle around the three words that rhyme. Draw a green box around the two words that rhyme.

Help finish the limerick below by filling in the blanks with a word from the Word Bank.

Word Bank				
class	lazy	pass	crazy	Daisy

There once was a student named __ __ __ __ __

Who wouldn't work because she was __ __ __ __

She slept during __ __ __ __ __.

No way she could __ __ __ __.

Her poor teacher finally went __ __ __ __ __.

💡 **Work with a partner and write a limerick. It helps to start with three rhyming words and two other rhyming words, then make up the sentences.**

A Tall Tale

 *A **tall tale** is a story about a superhuman hero. The story is funny because everything is exaggerated. That means it is much bigger and better than real life. Read the tall tale below. Use a yellow crayon or marker to highlight each thing that is exaggerated.*

Paul Bunyan

Paul Bunyan was a mighty man. He was so big, he had to use wagon wheels for buttons. Paul was a lumberjack. He owned a blue ox named Babe. Paul and Babe were so big that their tracks made 10,000 lakes in the state of Minnesota.

Paul worked with seven axmen. They were so big that they were six feet tall sitting down. All of them were named Elmer. So when Paul called "Elmer!" they all came running.

The year of the two winters, it got so cold that when the axmen would speak, their words froze in midair. When it thawed in the spring, there was a terrible chatter for weeks.

One time Paul caught two giant mosquitoes and used them to drill holes in maple trees.

Paul Bunyan had a purple cow named Lucy. In the year of two winters, it got so cold that Lucy's milk turned to ice cream before it hit the pail.

The End

 Choose two funny sentences above and copy them on another piece of paper. Then draw a picture about each one.

A Play

*A **play** is a story written as a script. Actors read the script, then memorize their lines, so they can pretend to be the characters in the story. Read the play below. The words in parentheses tell the actors what to do.*

A Bad Idea

(Megan and Kyle are talking before class starts.)

Megan: Hey, Kyle, are you ready for the big test today? I studied that list of words and the definitions for two hours last night.

Kyle: Oh, brother! I didn't study at all. I just wrote all the answers on the palm of my hand, see?

Megan: Kyle! You can't do that! That's cheating!

Kyle: Hey, don't worry. I won't get caught. Mrs. King will never know. *(Teacher passes out the tests.)*

Mrs. King: Okay, no more talking. Everyone keep your eyes on your own paper, and cover your answers with a cover sheet. You may begin. *(Kyle looks at his hand when the teacher isn't looking.)*

Joe: *(raising his hand)* Mrs. King, may I get a drink? I have the hiccups.

Mrs. King: Yes, you may.

Kyle: *(raising his hand)* Mrs. King, may I get a drink, too?

Mrs. King: Kyle, what is that on your hand? I think you better come to my desk.

Kyle: *(looks over at Megan)* Oh no . . .

Megan: Busted!

Use markers or crayons to follow each direction.

1. The words in parentheses are called *stage directions*. Underline all the stage directions with a blue line.

2. Highlight Megan's words in pink.

3. Highlight Kyle's words in yellow.

4. Highlight Mrs. King's words in green.

5. Highlight Joe's words in orange.

Scholastic Success With

CONTEMPORARY MANUSCRIPT

Aa

Trace and write.

A A A A

a a a a

Aa

Artist Anthony

asks for answers.

Bb

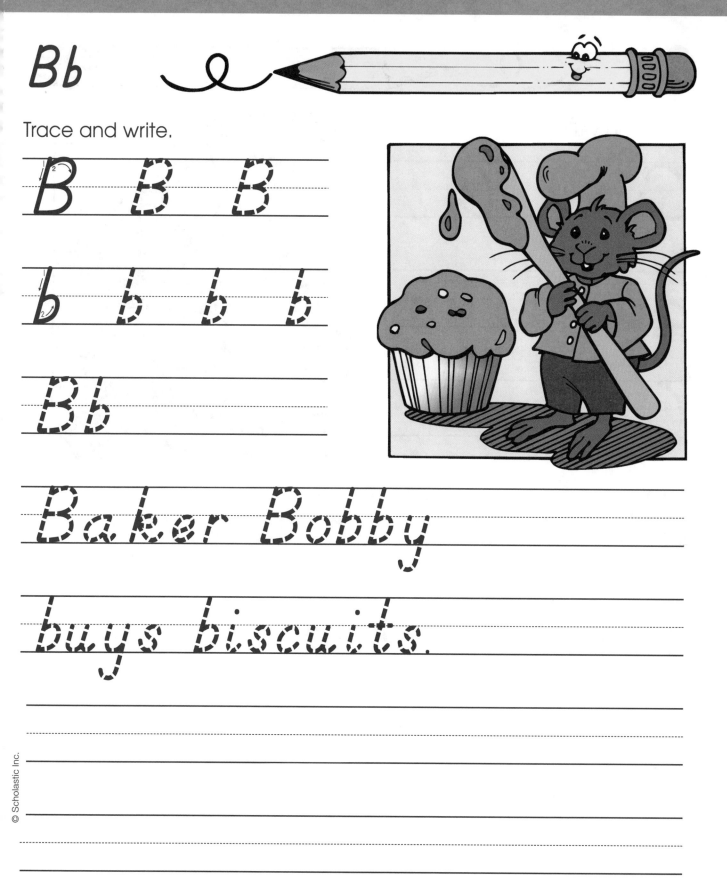

Trace and write.

B B B

b b b b

Bb

Baker Bobby

buys biscuits.

Cc

Trace and write.

C C C

c c c

Cc

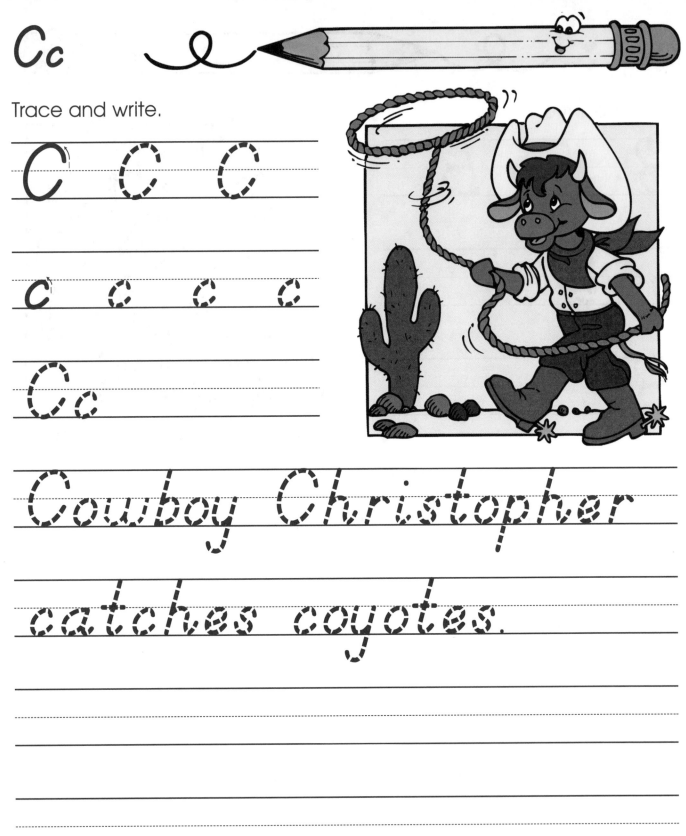

Cowboy Christopher

catches coyotes.

Dd

Trace and write.

D D D D

d d d d

Dd

Dancer Deandra

dances with ducks.

Ee

Trace and write.

E E E E

e e e e

Ee

Engineer Eduardo

enjoys eating.

Ff

Trace and write.

F F F

f f f f

F f

Firefighter Freda

feels fearless.

Gg

Trace and write.

G G G

g g g g

Gg

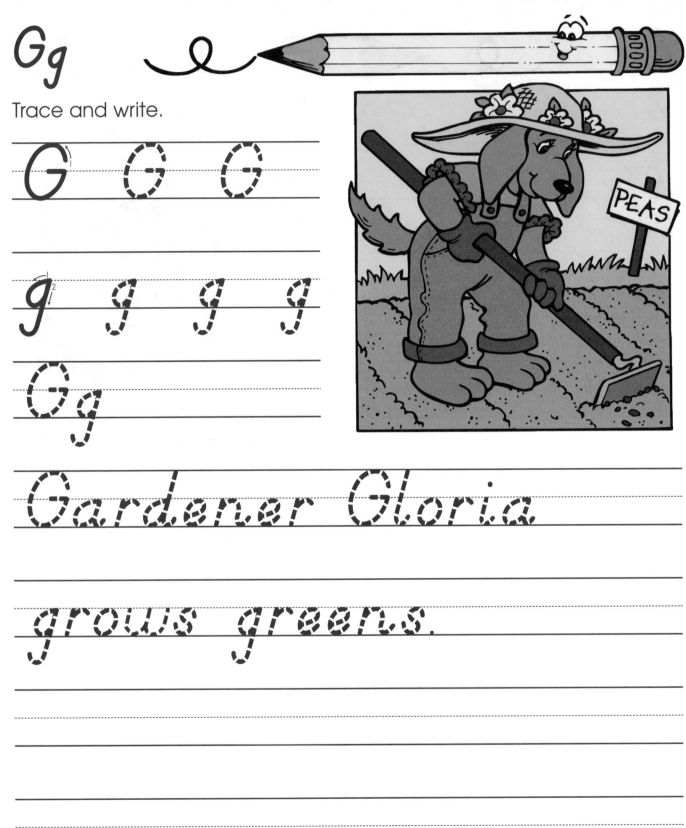

Gardener Gloria

grows greens.

Hh

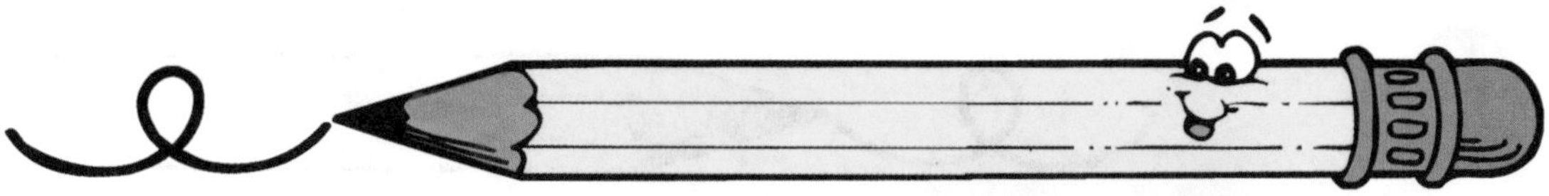

Trace and write.

H H H H

h h h h

Hh

Handyman Harry

helps Hazel Hippo.

Ii

Trace and write.

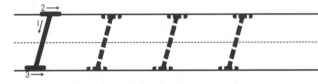

Inspector Irving

is investigating.

Jj

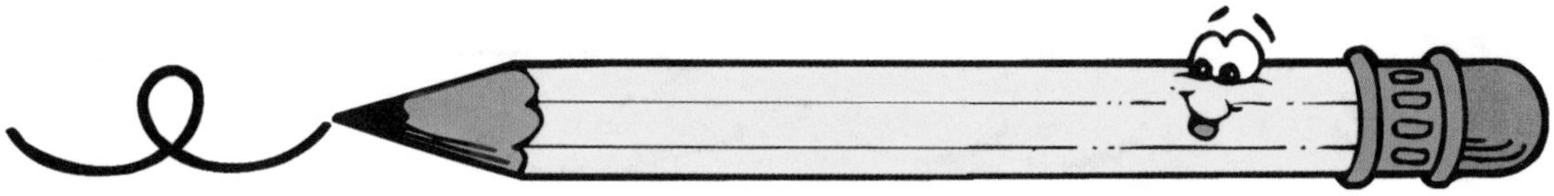

Trace and write.

J J J J

j j j j

Jj

Juggler Jeannie

jumps joyfully.

Kk

Trace and write.

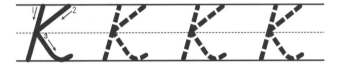

K k

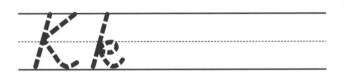

King Kevin kisses

kind kittens.

Ll

Trace and write.

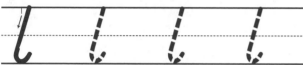

Reading is fun!

Librarian Louis

loves listening.

Mm

Trace and write.

M M M M

m m m m

Mm

Musician Matt

makes merry.

Nn

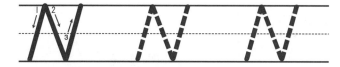

Trace and write.

N N N N

n n n n

Nn

Nurse Nancy

needs new patients.

Oo

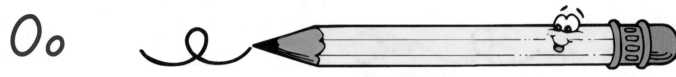

Trace and write.

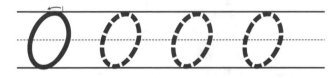

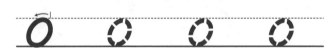

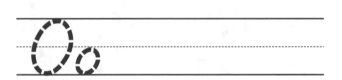

Optometrist Oliver

owns one octopus.

Pp

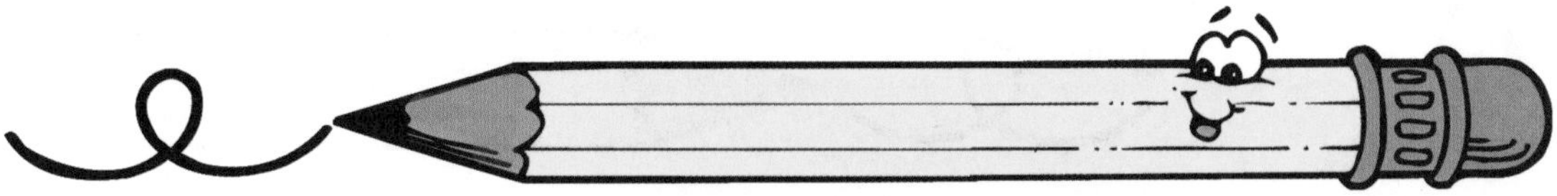

Trace and write.

P P P P

p p p p p

Pp

Postman Paul

piles packages.

Qq

Trace and write.

Q Q Q Q

q q q q

Qq

Queen Quiana

quilts quietly.

Rr

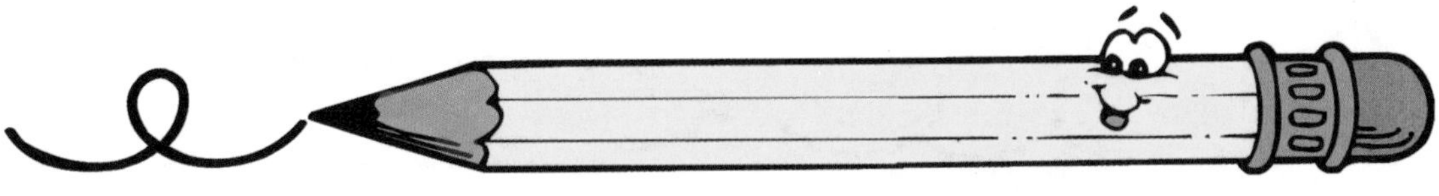

Trace and write.

R   R   R   R

r   r   r   r

Rr

Racer Rowena rides

rapidly to Rome.

Ss

Trace and write.

S S S S

s s s s

Ss

Sailor Susanna

sings sea songs.

Tt

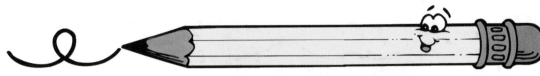

Trace and write.

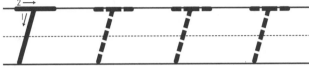

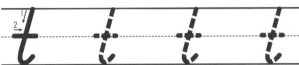

Teacher Tatiana

tells tall tales.

Uu

You're out!

Trace and write.

U U U

u u u u

Uu

Umpire Ulysses

upset Ursula.

Vv

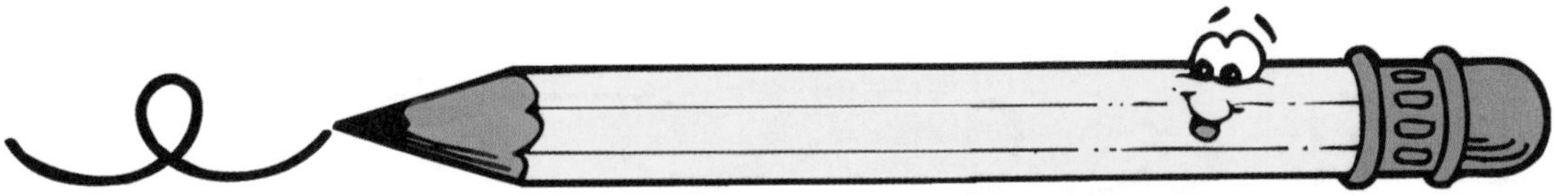

Trace and write.

V V V V

v v v v

Vv

Veterinarian Vince

visited Vermont.

Ww

Trace and write.

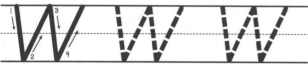

Ww

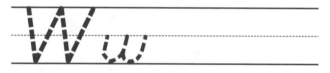

Weatherman Wes

went west.

Xx

Trace and write.

X X X X

X X X X

Xx

Explorer Xenia

is excited.

Yy

Trace and write.

Y Y Y Y

y y y y

Yy

Yachtsman Yves

yodels loudly.

Zz

Trace and write.

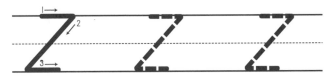

Zz

Zena Zeke

zooms to the zoo.

A–Z

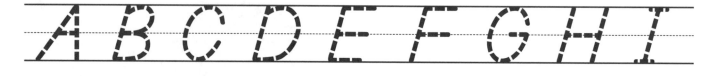

Trace and write.

A B C D E F G H I

J K L M N O P Q R

S T U V W X Y Z

a–z

Trace and write.

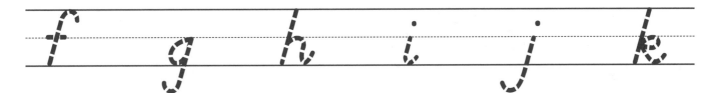

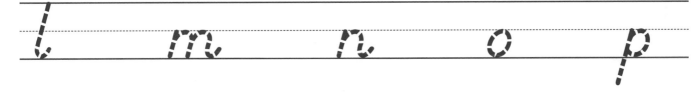

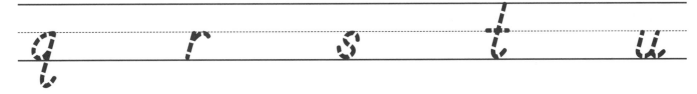

1–5

Trace and write.

1

2

3

4

5

6-10

Trace and write.

Color Words

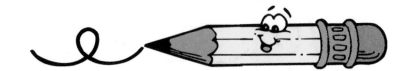

Trace and write.

red

yellow

blue

green

orange

yellow

red

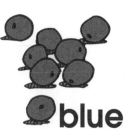
blue

green

orange

More Color Words

Trace and write.

purple

brown

black

white

pink

pink

white

purple

brown

black

Number Words

Trace and write.

1 one

2 two

3 three

4 four

5 five

More Number Words

Trace and write.

6 six

7 seven

8 eight

9 nine

10 ten

Shapes

Trace and write.

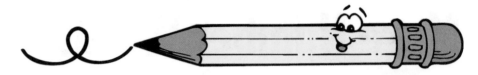

oval

heart

circle

square

triangle

diamond

rectangle

Days of the Week

Trace and write.

Sunday

Monday

Tuesday

Wednesday

Thursday

Friday

Saturday

Months

Jan.   Feb.   March   April   May   June

Trace and write.

January

February

March

April

May

June

Months

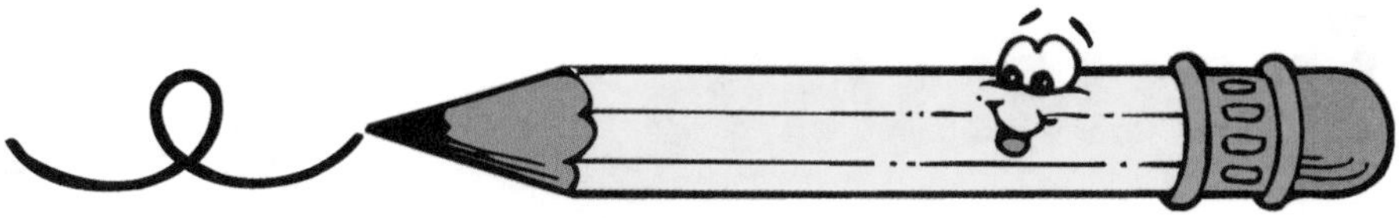

Trace and write.

July

August

September

October

November

December

Special Days

Write each
special day.

New Year's Day

Valentine's Day

Presidents' Day

St. Patrick's Day

Mother's Day

Father's Day

Fourth of July

Special Days

Write each special day.

AUG. SEPT. OCT. NOV. DEC.

Labor Day

Halloween

Veterans Day

Thanksgiving

Hannukah

Christmas

Kwanzaa

Careers From A to Z

Write the career names on the lines below.

astronaut
banker

chef
doctor

engineer
firefighter

grocer
hotel worker

inspector
janitor

Careers From A to Z

Write the career names on the lines below.

knitter	musician	professor	senator
lawyer	nurse	quilter	teacher
optometrist		reporter	

Careers From A to Z

Write the career names on the lines below.

umpire	X-ray technician
veterinarian	yoga instructor
weatherman	zookeeper

The Planets

Write the names of these planets.

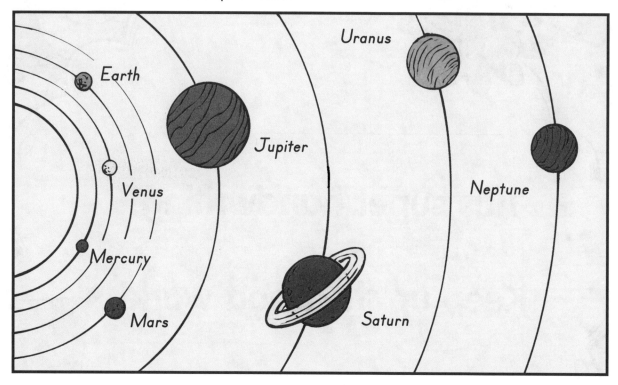

_____

- -

_____

_____

- -

_____

_____

- -

_____

_____

- -

_____

has super handwriting!

Keep up the good work!

_____
signed

_____
date

GRAMMAR

Telling Sentences and Questions

 *A **telling sentence** tells something. It begins with a capital letter and ends with a period. A **question** asks something. It begins with a capital letter and ends with a question mark.*

Read each sentence. Write T on the line if the sentence is a telling sentence. Write Q on the line if it is a question.

1 I took my pet to see the vet. _____

2 Was your pet sick? _____

3 What did the vet do? _____

4 The vet checked my pet. _____

5 The vet said my pet had a cold. _____

The order of the words in a sentence can change its meaning.
Write T next to the sentence that is a telling sentence.
Write Q next to the sentence that is a question.

6 Is your pet well now? _____

7 Now your pet is well. _____

Telling Sentences and Questions

*A **telling sentence** tells something. It begins with a capital letter and ends with a period. A **question** asks something. It begins with a capital letter and ends with a question mark.*

Underline the capital letter that begins each sentence. Add a period (.) if it is a telling sentence. Add a question mark (?) if it is a question.

1 The vet is nice _____

2 She helped my dog _____

3 Did she see your cat _____

4 Is the cat well now _____

5 My cat feels better _____

The order of the words in a sentence can change its meaning. Change the word order in the telling sentence to make it a question. Write the question.

6 He will take the cat home.

_____

Telling Sentences and Questions

Look at the underlined part of each sentence. If it is written correctly, fill in the last bubble. If not, fill in the bubble next to the correct answer.

1 The <u>girl</u> likes dogs.
- ⟶ the girl
- ⟶ Girl the
- ⟶ correct as is

2 <u>the vet</u> helps sick pets.
- ⟶ the Vet
- ⟶ The vet
- ⟶ correct as is

3 The boy likes <u>cats?</u>
- ⟶ cats.
- ⟶ cats
- ⟶ correct as is

4 Is the vet <u>nice?</u>
- ⟶ nice
- ⟶ nice.
- ⟶ correct as is

5 <u>do you</u> have a pet?
- ⟶ Do You
- ⟶ Do you
- ⟶ correct as is

6 <u>Is when</u> the vet open?
- ⟶ When is
- ⟶ when Is
- ⟶ correct as is

7 <u>he has</u> a bird.
- ⟶ Has he
- ⟶ He has
- ⟶ correct as is

8 My dog likes <u>the vet?</u>
- ⟶ The vet.
- ⟶ the vet.
- ⟶ correct as is

9 Who has a <u>goldfish.</u>
- ⟶ goldfish?
- ⟶ goldfish
- ⟶ correct as is

10 <u>will you</u> see the vet again?
- ⟶ Will you
- ⟶ You
- ⟶ correct as is

Exclamations and Commands

 *An **exclamation** shows strong feelings, such as excitement, surprise, or fear. It begins with a capital letter and ends with an exclamation mark (!).*

*A **command** makes a request or tells someone to do something. It ends with a period or an exclamation mark.*

Read each sentence. Write E if the sentence is an exclamation. Write C if the sentence is a command.

1 Ruby copies Angela! ———

2 Look at their dresses. ———

3 They're exactly the same! ———

4 Angela is mad! ———

5 Look at Ruby! ———

6 Show Angela how Ruby hops. ———

Write each sentence correctly.

Exclamation be yourself

7 _____

Command don't copy other people

8 _____

Exclamations and Commands

An **exclamation** *shows strong feelings, such as excitement, surprise, or fear. It begins with a capital letter and ends with an exclamation mark (!).*

A **command** *makes a request or tells someone to do something. It ends with a period or an exclamation mark.*

Read each exclamation. Use words from the box to tell what strong feeling it shows.

excitement	fear	anger	surprise

1 I lost my jacket. I'll be so cold! _____

2 Look what I have! _____

3 I didn't know you had my jacket! _____

4 Give it to me now! _____

Look at the picture.

5 Circle the command that goes with the picture.

Please don't be upset!   Wear your new hat.

6 Write another command for the picture.

_____

7 Write an exclamation for the picture.

_____

Exclamations and Commands

Read each exclamation. If it is written correctly, fill in the last bubble.
If not, fill in the bubble next to the correct way to write it.

1 You are a great hopper

- ○ you are a great hopper!
- ○ you are a great hopper.
- ○ You are a great hopper!
- ○ correct as is

2 the picture looks beautiful.

- ○ The picture looks beautiful!
- ○ The picture looks beautiful
- ○ the picture looks beautiful!
- ○ correct as is

3 i can paint, too!

- ○ i can paint, too
- ○ I can paint, too!
- ○ I can paint, too
- ○ correct as is

4 I did it!

- ○ i did it!
- ○ I did it
- ○ i did it
- ○ correct as is

Read each command. If it is written correctly, fill in the last bubble.
If not, fill in the bubble next to the correct way to write it.

5 teach me how to hop.

- ○ teach me how to hop
- ○ Teach me how to hop
- ○ Teach me how to hop.
- ○ correct as is

6 Hop backward like this

- ○ Hop backward like this.
- ○ hop backward like this
- ○ hop backward like this!
- ○ correct as is

Types of Sentences; Capital I

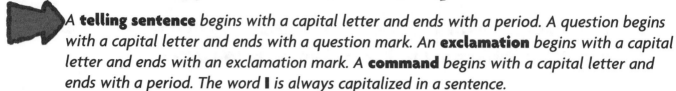A **telling sentence** begins with a capital letter and ends with a period. A question begins with a capital letter and ends with a question mark. An **exclamation** begins with a capital letter and ends with an exclamation mark. A **command** begins with a capital letter and ends with a period. The word **I** is always capitalized in a sentence.

Read each sentence. Circle the beginning letter, end punctuation, and the word I in each sentence.

1 I sail my boat in the lake.

2 May I have a turn?

3 I am so happy!

4 Can Kiku and I play?

5 Bill and I fly the kite.

Write each sentence in the correct box.

Telling Sentences

_____

_____

Questions

_____

_____

Exclamation _____

© Scholastic Inc.

Types of Sentences; Capital I

A **telling sentence** begins with a capital letter and ends with a period. A **question** begins with a capital letter and ends with a question mark. An **exclamation** begins with a capital letter and ends with an exclamation mark. A **command** begins with a capital letter and ends with a period. The word **I** is always capitalized in a sentence.

Decide if each sentence is a telling sentence, a question, an exclamation,or a command. Write T, Q, E, or C on the lines.

1 My sister and I went to the lake. _____

2 Come see this. _____

3 I saw three little sailboats. _____

4 Put the boat in the water. _____

5 Did I have a good time? _____

6 You bet! I loved it! _____

7 Can I go again soon? _____

What would you do at the lake? Use the word I and your own ideas to finish the sentences.

8 At the lake _____ saw _____ .

9 _____ can _____ .

10 My friend and _____ liked _____ best.

© Scholastic Inc.

Types of Sentences; Capital I

Read each sentence. If it is written correctly, fill in the last bubble. If not, fill in the bubble next to the correct way to write it.

1 i have fun with my bike.

- ⬭ I have fun with my bike.
- ⬭ I have fun with my bike
- ⬭ i have fun with my bike
- ⬭ correct as is

2 can I ride to the beach

- ⬭ Can I ride to the beach
- ⬭ Can I ride to the beach?
- ⬭ Can i ride to the beach?
- ⬭ correct as is

3 i find a pretty shell

- ⬭ I find a pretty shell
- ⬭ i find a pretty shell.
- ⬭ I find a pretty shell.
- ⬭ correct as is

4 Jill and I see a crab.

- ⬭ Jill and I see a crab
- ⬭ Jill and i see a crab.
- ⬭ Jill and i see a crab
- ⬭ correct as is

5 get the shovel

- ⬭ Get the shovel
- ⬭ Get the shovel.
- ⬭ get the shovel.
- ⬭ correct as is

6 what a mess I made

- ⬭ What a mess I made!
- ⬭ What a mess I made
- ⬭ what a mess I made!
- ⬭ correct as is

© Scholastic Inc.

Common Nouns

Common nouns *name people, places, or things.*

Read each sentence. Circle the common nouns.

1 The boy made a boat.

2 The brothers went to the park.

3 A girl was with her grandmother.

4 Two boats crashed in the lake.

5 Friends used a needle and thread to fix the sail.

Write the common nouns you circled under the correct heading below.

People	Places	Things
_____	_____	_____
_____	_____	_____
_____		_____
_____		_____
_____		_____

Common Nouns

 Common nouns *name people, places, or things.*

Help sort the cards. Some of the words are nouns. Some are not.
Circle the nouns.

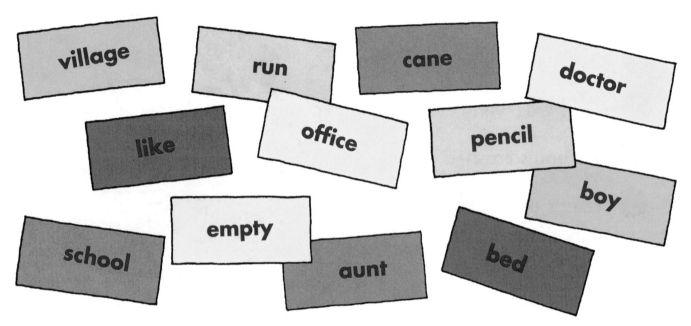

village
run
cane
doctor
like
office
pencil
boy
empty
school
aunt
bed

Write each noun you circled under the correct heading.

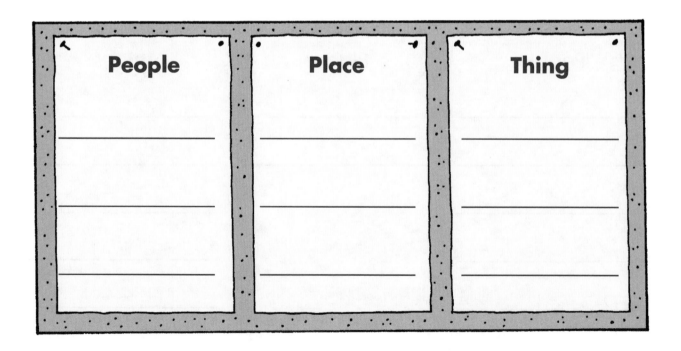

People	Place	Thing

© Scholastic Inc.

Common Nouns

Common nouns *name people, places, or things.*

Complete each sentence about the picture.
Use the nouns in the Word Bank below.

Word Bank

| bench | bridge | carousel | children | stream | swing |

1 The _____ is near the tree.

2 The _____ is beside the slide.

3 The _____ are playing in the park.

4 The _____ has six sections.

5 The _____ is over the stream.

6 The _____ runs through the park.

Common Nouns

Look at the underlined word in each sentence. If it is a common noun, fill in the bubble next to yes. If it is not a common noun, fill in the bubble next to no.

1 Our class <u>went</u> on a trip.

   ○ yes   ○ no

2 We went to the <u>city</u>.

   ○ yes   ○ no

3 The buildings were <u>tall</u>.

   ○ yes   ○ no

4 There were many <u>cars</u>.

   ○ yes   ○ no

A common noun is underlined in each sentence. Tell if it names a person, place or thing. Fill in the bubble next to the correct answer.

5 We went into a big <u>room</u>.

   ○ person   ○ place   ○ thing

6 Our <u>teacher</u> led us.

   ○ person   ○ place   ○ thing

7 I walked with my best <u>friend</u>.

   ○ person   ○ place   ○ thing

8 We sat at a long <u>table</u>.

   ○ person   ○ place   ○ thing

Capitalize Names and Places

Special names of people and places always begin with capital letters. They are called **proper nouns**.

Read each sentence. Circle the proper noun.

1 George Ancona is a photographer.

2 His parents came from Mexico.

3 His family called him Jorgito.

4 They lived in Coney Island.

5 Now he travels to Honduras to take pictures.

6 Tio Mario worked in a sign shop.

Write the proper nouns you circled under the correct heading below.

People   **Places**

_____   _____

_____   _____

_____   _____

Capitalize Names and Places

 Special names of people and places always begin with capital letters. They are called **proper nouns**.

Read the postcard. Find the proper nouns. Write them correctly on the lines below.

Dear sue,

It's very hot here in california. We visited the city of los angeles. Then we swam in the pacific ocean. I miss you.

Love,

tonya

sue wong
11 shore road
austin, texas 78728

1 _____

2 _____

3 _____

4 _____

5 _____

6 _____

7 _____

8 _____

Write a sentence with a proper noun. Underline the capital letter or letters in the proper noun. Then write whether it names a person or a place.

_____

_____

Capitalize Names and Places

A proper noun is underlined in each sentence. Does it name a person or a place? Fill in the bubble next to the correct answer.

1 <u>Betty</u> is a photographer.

○ person   ○ place

2 She goes to <u>Florida</u> to take pictures.

○ person   ○ place

3 She meets her older brother <u>Peter</u>.

○ person   ○ place

4 She takes his picture in a city called <u>Miami</u>.

○ person   ○ place

Read each sentence. Find the proper noun. Fill in the bubble next to the word that is a proper noun.

5 Their friend is Emilio.

○ friend   ○ Emilio
○ Their   ○ is

6 They all went to Orlando.

○ Orlando   ○ all
○ They   ○ went

7 They visited Disney World there.

○ They
○ there
○ visited
○ Disney World

8 They walked down Main Street in the park.

○ park
○ walked
○ They
○ Main Street

Verbs

 *A **verb** is an action word. It tells what someone or something is doing.*

Read each sentence. Write the action verb in the telling part of the sentence.

1 Ronald runs to the field. _____

2 Michael wears a batting helmet. _____

3 He smacks the ball hard. _____

4 Ronald holds the wrong end of the bat. _____

5 He misses the ball. _____

6 Ronald waits in left field. _____

7 He writes G for great. _____

8 Ronald's father helps him. _____

Write a sentence about the picture. Use an action verb and circle it.

_____

_____

_____

Verbs

 *A **verb** is an action word. It tells what someone or something is doing.*

Draw a line to match each sentence with an action verb. Then write the action verbs on the lines to finish the sentences.

1 Moms and dads _____ the game.   throws

2 The pitcher _____ the ball.   opens

3 Ronald _____ his eyes.   watch

4 The team _____ for Ronald.   cheers

5 Ronald _____ the ball past the pitcher.   runs

6 He _____ to first base.   hits

7 Someone _____, "Go Ronald go!"   eat

8 The kids _____ ice cream after the game.   yells

Verbs

Look at the underlined word in each sentence. Fill in the correct bubble to tell whether or not it is an action verb.

1 The dog <u>runs</u> down the road.
- ⬭ action verb
- ⬭ not an action verb

2 The girl chases the <u>dog</u>.
- ⬭ action verb
- ⬭ not an action verb

3 The dog finds a <u>bone</u>.
- ⬭ action verb
- ⬭ not an action verb

4 The <u>sun</u> sets.
- ⬭ action verb
- ⬭ not an action verb

5 Rain <u>falls</u> from the sky.
- ⬭ action verb
- ⬭ not an action verb

6 The girl <u>splashes</u> water.
- ⬭ action verb
- ⬭ not an action verb

7 The dog hides <u>under</u> a bush.
- ⬭ action verb
- ⬭ not an action verb

8 The girl <u>finds</u> the dog.
- ⬭ action verb
- ⬭ not an action verb

9 The sun <u>shines</u>.
- ⬭ action verb
- ⬭ not an action verb

10 The girl sees a <u>rainbow</u>.
- ⬭ action verb
- ⬭ not an action verb

Simple Sentences

 *A **simple sentence** has a naming part and a telling part. It tells a complete thought.*

Read each group of words. Put an X next to it if it is a complete thought. Circle the naming part and underline the telling part in each sentence.

1 One day thirsty _____

2 Crow could not get a drink. _____

3 The water rose. _____

4 The old mouse _____

5 Put the bell _____

6 One mouse had a plan. _____

Write a simple sentence about the picture below.
Circle the naming part and underline the telling part.

_____

Simple Sentences

*A **simple sentence** has a naming part and a telling part. It tells a complete thought.*

Circle the sentence in each pair. Then underline the naming part of the sentence.

1   (a)   Lin likes to play soccer.

      (b)   likes to play soccer

2   (a)   Her friends

      (b)   Her friends watch her play.

3   (a)   They cheer for Lin.

      (b)   They cheer for

4   (a)   Her mom goes to all of her games.

      (b)   goes to all of her games

5   (a)   The coach is very proud of Lin.

      (b)   The coach is

Simple Sentences

Read each sentence. Fill in the bubble to tell if the underlined words are the naming or the telling part of the sentence. Some of the underlined words may not be the whole part.

1 The cat <u>was under the tree.</u>
- ○ naming part
- ○ telling part
- ○ not the whole part

2 <u>A bird</u> saw the cat.
- ○ naming part
- ○ telling part
- ○ not the whole part

3 The bird <u>flew</u> away.
- ○ naming part
- ○ telling part
- ○ not the whole part

4 <u>Then, the</u> cat walked away.
- ○ naming part
- ○ telling part
- ○ not the whole part

Fill in the bubble to choose a naming or telling part that makes a sentence.

5 The bird ____.
- ○ in the tall tree
- ○ saw the cat go away
- ○ flying very fast in the sky

6 ____ came back to the tree.
- ○ Deep in the woods
- ○ The large and pretty
- ○ Then the bird

7 ____ saw the bird.
- ○ After a minute, the cat
- ○ Running across the grass
- ○ The cat was watching

8 So the cat ____.
- ○ walking to the tree
- ○ under the tree
- ○ walked back, too

Past-Tense Verbs

*Some verbs add **-ed** to tell about actions that happened in the past.*

Find the past-tense verb in each sentence. Write it on the line.

1 Last spring, Daisy planted a garden. _____

2 Floyd watered the garden. _____

3 Together they weeded their garden. _____

4 One day they discovered a big carrot. _____

Read each sentence. If the sentence has a past-tense verb, write it on the line. If the sentence does not have a past-tense verb, leave the line blank.

5 They like to eat carrots. _____

6 They pulled on the carrot. _____

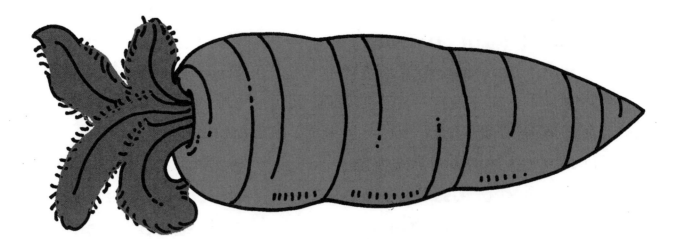

Past-Tense Verbs

 *Some verbs add **-ed** to tell about actions that happened in the past.*

Read the first sentence in each pair. Change the underlined verb to tell about the past.

1 Today my dogs <u>push</u> open the back door.

Yesterday my dogs _____ open the back door.

2 Today they <u>splash</u> in the rain puddles.

Last night they _____ in the rain puddles.

3 Now they <u>roll</u> in the mud.

Last week they _____ in the mud.

4 Today I <u>follow</u> my dogs' footprints.

Last Sunday I _____ my dogs' footprints.

5 Now I <u>wash</u> my dogs from head to toe.

Earlier I _____ my dogs from head to toe.

Write a sentence using one of the verbs you wrote.

_____

_____

_____

Past-Tense Verbs

Read each sentence. Look at the underlined verb. If it is not correct, fill in the bubble next to the correct verb. If it is correct, fill in the last bubble.

1 Last Saturday I <u>visit</u> John in the country.
○ visited
○ correct as is

2 Two weeks ago we <u>watched</u> a sailboat race.
○ watch
○ correct as is

3 A week ago we <u>walked</u> to the top of a big hill.
○ walk
○ correct as is

4 Last week I <u>talk</u> to John on the phone.
○ talked
○ correct as is

5 Earlier I <u>ask</u> him to visit me in the city.
○ asked
○ correct as is

6 Friday morning his train <u>pulled</u> into the station.
○ pull
○ correct as is

7 Last night my dog <u>barked</u> when he saw John.
○ bark
○ correct as is

8 Yesterday I <u>show</u> John around the city.
○ showed
○ correct as is

Pronouns

 *A **pronoun** takes the place of the name of a person, place, or thing.*

Read each pair of sentences. Circle the pronoun in the second sentence of each pair. Then write what the pronoun stands for. The first one has been done for you.

1 Wendell did not like to clean his room.

(He) liked a messy room. _____Wendell_____

2 Mother wanted Wendell to do some work.

She handed Wendell a broom. _____

3 The pigs came into Wendell's room.

They helped Wendell clean the room. _____

4 Wendell and the pigs played a board game.

Wendell and the pigs had fun playing it. _____

5 The pigs and Wendell played for a long time.

They liked to play games. _____

6 Wendell was sad to see his friends go.

He liked playing with the pigs. _____

Pronouns

A **pronoun** *takes the place of the name of a person, place, or thing.*

Read the story. Use the pronouns in the box to complete each sentence. The first one has been done for you.

they he she it

Glenda was walking in the woods. At last _____she_____

came to a house. _____1_____ was empty. She opened the door

and saw three chairs by the fireplace. _____2_____ were all

different sizes. She sat down on the smallest one. _____3_____

was the perfect size for her. Soon _____4_____ fell asleep.

When she woke up, three pigs were

standing over her. The father pig spoke. _____5_____

asked Glenda if she would stay for dinner. "I would love to!"

said Glenda.

Pronouns

Read each sentence. Fill in the bubble next to the word or words that the underlined pronoun stands for.

1 <u>She</u> did not like the mess.
- ◯ Wendell
- ◯ The boy
- ◯ The pigs
- ◯ Mrs. Fultz

2 <u>He</u> did not like brooms.
- ◯ The pigs
- ◯ The boys
- ◯ The boy
- ◯ Mrs. Fultz

3 <u>It</u> was full of pigs.
- ◯ The rooms
- ◯ The house
- ◯ The pigs
- ◯ The door

4 <u>They</u> wanted to play.
- ◯ The room
- ◯ Wendell
- ◯ The pigs
- ◯ Mrs. Fultz

Read each sentence. Fill in the bubble next to the pronoun that can take the place of the underlined word or words.

5 <u>Wendell</u> waved good-bye to the pigs.
- ◯ He
- ◯ She
- ◯ It
- ◯ They

6 Wendell hoped <u>the pigs</u> would come back.
- ◯ it
- ◯ he
- ◯ they
- ◯ she

Types of Sentences

A **telling sentence** *tells something.* A **question** *asks something.* An **exclamation** *shows strong feelings.* A **command** *makes a request or gives a command.*

Read each sentence. Write it next to the correct heading.

What a big mango!   I like mangos.

Is that a banana?   Did you find the fruit?

Buy me an avocado.   Come over for dinner.

I want to eat dinner.   This tastes great!

Exclamation: _____

_____

Command: _____

_____

Question: _____

_____

Telling Sentence: _____

_____

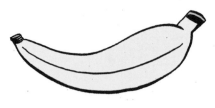

Types of Sentences

A **telling sentence** *tells something. A* **question** *asks something. An* **exclamation** *shows strong feelings. A* **command** *makes a request or gives a command.*

Read the following sentences. Write the correct end punctuation mark for each sentence. Then write the sentence type on the line to the right of each sentence. Write T for each telling sentence or statement, Q for each question, E for each exclamation, and C for each command.

1 We're going to the beach __   _____

2 Do you have your bathing suit __   _____

3 We will play in the sand __   _____

4 Pack the sunscreen __   _____

5 I love swimming __   _____

6 Take the beach chair __   _____

7 What time do we leave __   _____

8 Wow, that's a huge wave __   _____

Types of Sentences

Read each sentence. Fill in the bubble next to the correct type of sentence.

1 Give me that apple.

○ telling ○ question ○ exclamation ○ command

2 What kind of fruit is this?

○ telling ○ question ○ exclamation ○ command

3 What a great dinner!

○ telling ○ question ○ exclamation ○ command

4 Buy this watermelon.

○ telling ○ question ○ exclamation ○ command

5 This is the best watermelon!

○ telling ○ question ○ exclamation ○ command

6 I would like to have another piece.

○ telling ○ question ○ exclamation ○ command

7 Are those bananas ripe?

○ telling ○ question ○ exclamation ○ command

8 A mango is smaller than a watermelon.

○ telling ○ question ○ exclamation ○ command

Word Order

Words in a sentence must be in an order that makes sense.

Read each group of words. Write the words in the correct order to make a statement. Begin each statement with a capital letter and end it with a period.

1 brothers two can live together

_____

2 Hungbu find will a home new

_____

3 will fix Mother the house

_____

Read each group of words. Write the words in the correct order to make a question. Begin each question with a capital letter and end it with a question mark.

4 clean you will house the

_____

5 help can the bird them

_____

Word Order

Words in a sentence must be in an order that makes sense.

Write the words in the correct order to make a sentence. Then write if the sentence is a question or a statement.

1 find Will I some wood? _____

_____

2 must Each of help us. _____

_____

3 trees are the Where? _____

_____

Write each group of words in the correct order to make a statement. Then write them in the correct order to make a question. Add capital letters and end punctuation to your sentences.

4 your pumpkin is that _____

_____

5 help cut you can pumpkin the _____

_____

Word Order

Read each group of words. If the word order does not make sense, fill in the bubble next to the correct word order. If the words are in an order that makes sense, fill in the last bubble.

1 Dad made breakfast for eggs.
- ○ Made for breakfast Dad eggs.
- ○ Dad made breakfast eggs for.
- ○ Dad made eggs for breakfast.
- ○ correct as is

2 Open eggs four he cracked.
- ○ He cracked eggs open four.
- ○ He cracked open four eggs.
- ○ Four eggs cracked open he.
- ○ correct as is

3 Like do eggs you?
- ○ Eggs do you like?
- ○ Do you like eggs?
- ○ Do eggs like you?
- ○ correct as is

4 Help did you him?
- ○ Did help you him?
- ○ Did you help him?
- ○ Help you did him?
- ○ correct as is

5 With fork a beat eggs.
- ○ Beat eggs with a fork.
- ○ Eggs beat a fork with.
- ○ A fork beat with eggs.
- ○ correct as is

6 Do you want some toast?
- ○ Do you toast some want?
- ○ Do some toast want you?
- ○ You want do some toast?
- ○ correct as is

Plural Nouns

 *Most nouns add **-s** to mean more than one. Nouns that end in **s**, **x**, **ch**, or **sh** add **-es** to mean more than one.*

Read the sentences. Underline the plural nouns. Circle the letter or letters that were added to mean more than one.

1 We have two accordions in our house.

2 Grandma has many brushes to fix her hair.

3 My grandfather has many clocks and watches.

4 A lot of flowers are in the boxes.

Write the nouns that add -s.

_____

Write the nouns that add -es.

_____

Plural Nouns

 *Most nouns add **-s** to mean more than one. Nouns that end in **s**, **x**, **ch**, or **sh** add **-es** to mean more than one.*

Read each sentence. Add -s or -es to the noun at the end of the sentence to make it plural. Write it in the sentence.

1 Dad made five cheese _____. (sandwich)

2 He packed five _____ for the children. (lunch)

3 Lisa put fruit in all the _____. (lunchbox)

4 She packed some paper _____, **too.** (dish)

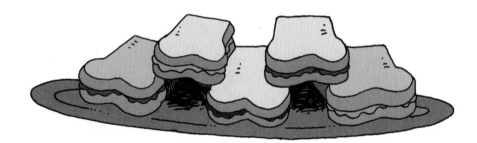

Write the plural for each noun on the line.

5 one box

two _____

6 one dress

two _____

7 one coat

two _____

8 one bench

two _____

Plural Nouns

Read each pair of nouns. If the plural noun is correct, fill in the last bubble. If it is not correct, fill in the bubble next to the correct plural noun.

1 sketch, sketchs
- ⬭ sketches
- ⬭ correct as is

2 tree, trees
- ⬭ treess
- ⬭ correct as is

3 fox, foxs
- ⬭ foxes
- ⬭ correct as is

4 paint, paints
- ⬭ paintes
- ⬭ correct as is

5 squirrel, squirrels
- ⬭ squirreles
- ⬭ correct as is

6 dress, dressees
- ⬭ dresses
- ⬭ correct as is

7 ball, balles
- ⬭ balls
- ⬭ correct as is

8 wish, wishes
- ⬭ wishs
- ⬭ correct as is

Adjectives

 An **adjective** describes a person, place, or thing. Color, size, and number words are adjectives.

Read each sentence. Underline the nouns. Write the adjective that tells about each noun.

1 The brown donkey carried the heavy sack.

_____ _____

2 The striped cat chased two birds.

_____ _____

3 The little rooster crowed six times.

_____ _____

Write the adjectives from the sentences above.

4 Write the adjectives that tell what kind.

_____

5 Write the adjectives that tell how many.

_____

Adjectives

An **adjective** describes a person, place, or thing. Color, size, and number words are adjectives.

Read each sentence. Find the adjective and the noun it describes. Circle the noun. Write the adjective on the line.

1 Peggy and Rosa went to the big zoo. _____

2 They looked up at the tall giraffe. _____

3 The giraffe looked down at the two girls. _____

4 The giraffe had brown spots. _____

Write adjectives from the sentences in the chart.

Color Word	Size Words	Number Word
_____	_____	_____
	_____	

© Scholastic Inc.

Adjectives

Read each sentence. Fill in the bubble next to the word that is an adjective.

1 In the morning, Jenny put on red boots.

- ⚪ put
- ⚪ boots
- ⚪ red
- ⚪ on

2 She found a yellow hat in the closet.

- ⚪ She
- ⚪ hat
- ⚪ found
- ⚪ yellow

3 She opened her purple umbrella.

- ⚪ opened
- ⚪ She
- ⚪ umbrella
- ⚪ purple

4 Jenny walked past a big house.

- ⚪ big
- ⚪ house
- ⚪ walked
- ⚪ past

5 She waved to three friends.

- ⚪ waved
- ⚪ three
- ⚪ to
- ⚪ friends

6 A little puppy trotted behind her.

- ⚪ trotted
- ⚪ puppy
- ⚪ little
- ⚪ behind

7 She jumped over a huge puddle.

- ⚪ She
- ⚪ jumped
- ⚪ huge
- ⚪ puddle

8 Two birds took a drink of water.

- ⚪ birds
- ⚪ of
- ⚪ took
- ⚪ Two

Verb *to be*

 Am, **is**, **are**, **was**, *and* **were** *are forms of the verb* **to be**. *These verbs show being instead of action.*

Read each sentence. Underline the verb. Write *past* if the sentence tells about the past. Write *now* if the sentence tells about the present.

1 The story is perfect. _____

2 The producers are happy. _____

3 The actors were funny. _____

4 The movie studio is interested in the story. _____

5 I am excited about the movie. _____

6 I was sad at the end. _____

© Scholastic Inc.

Verb *to be*

Am, **is, are**, **was**, *and* **were** *are forms of the verb* **to be**. *These verbs show being instead of action.*

Choose a verb from the box to finish each sentence. There may be more than one right answer. Write *one* if the sentence tells about one. Write *more* if it tells about more than one.

am	is	are	was	were

1 The movie _____ long. _____

2 She _____ in the movie. _____

3 They _____ at the movie theater yesterday. _____

4 The producers _____ spending money now. _____

5 The director _____ not at work yesterday. _____

6 The actors _____ acting now. _____

Verb *to be*

Read each sentence. Fill in the bubble next to the words that correctly tell about the sentence.

1 The movie was very long.
- ◯ past, more than one
- ◯ present, more than one
- ◯ past, one
- ◯ present, one

2 The seats at the movies are high up.
- ◯ past, more than one
- ◯ present, more than one
- ◯ past, one
- ◯ present, one

3 The actors were all big stars.
- ◯ past, more than one
- ◯ present, more than one
- ◯ past, one
- ◯ present, one

4 The scenes were interesting.
- ◯ past, more than one
- ◯ present, more than one
- ◯ past, one
- ◯ present, one

5 The trees and flowers were so beautiful.
- ◯ past, more than one
- ◯ present, more than one
- ◯ past, one
- ◯ present, one

6 I am going to see the movie again.
- ◯ past, more than one
- ◯ present, more than one
- ◯ past, one
- ◯ present, one

Irregular Verbs *go, do*

Irregular verbs change their spelling when they tell about the past. **Did** *is the past form of* **do** *and* **does**. **Went** *is the past form of* **go** *and* **goes**.

Read each sentence. Write present if the underlined verb tells about action now. Write past if it tells about action in the past.

Present	Past
go, goes	went
do, does	did

1 Grace <u>goes</u> to the playground. _____

2 Some other children <u>go</u>, too. _____

3 Grace <u>does</u> a scene from a story. _____

4 The children <u>do</u> the scene with her. _____

5 Grace <u>went</u> into battle as Joan of Arc. _____

6 She <u>did</u> the part of Anansi the Spider, too. _____

7 In another part, Grace <u>went</u> inside a
wooden horse. _____

8 She <u>did</u> many other parts. _____

Irregular Verbs *go, do*

Irregular verbs change their spelling when they tell about the past. **Did** *is the past form of* **do** *and* **does.** **Went** *is the past form of* **go** *and* **goes**.

Choose the correct word from the chart and write it on the line.

In the Present	In the Past
go, goes	went
do, does	did

1 Last week our family _____ to the art museum.

2 Pablo _____ there a lot.

3 His mother _____ the displays there now.

4 She _____ a new one yesterday.

5 _____ you want to join us tomorrow?

6 We want to _____ after lunch again.

Irregular Verbs *go, do*

Fill in the bubble next to the word that correctly completes the sentence.

1 Rose ____ to the ballet.
- ○ go
- ○ did
- ○ goes

2 Two dancers ____ a kick and a turn.
- ○ do
- ○ does
- ○ goes

3 Another dancer ____ a hop and a jump.
- ○ went
- ○ does
- ○ do

4 They ____ around in circles very fast.
- ○ goes
- ○ did
- ○ go

5 A girl ____ two big splits.
- ○ do
- ○ did
- ○ went

6 Then she ____ off stage.
- ○ go
- ○ did
- ○ went

7 Rose ____ home feeling very happy.
- ○ went
- ○ did
- ○ go

8 She ____ some of the steps, too.
- ○ do
- ○ did
- ○ goes

Quotation Marks

Quotation marks *show the exact words someone says. They go before the speaker's first word. They also go after the speaker's last word and the end punctuation mark.*

Read each sentence. Underline the exact words the speaker says. Put the words in quotation marks. The first one is done for you.

1 Max said, "Let's go on a picnic."

2 Cori replied,   That's a great idea.

3 Andy asked,   What should we bring?

4 Max said with a laugh,   We should bring food.

5 Cori added,   Yes, let's bring lots and lots of food.

6 Andy giggled and said,   You're no help at all!

Finish the sentences below by writing what Max, Cori, and Andy might say next. Use quotation marks.

7 Max said, _____.

8 Cori asked, _____.

9 Andy answered, _____.

Quotation Marks

Quotation marks *show the exact words someone says. They go before the speaker's first word. They also go after the speaker's last word and the end punctuation mark.*

Read the sentences. Then put quotation marks where they belong. The first one has been done for you.

1 Jan cried, "It is raining!"

2 She asked,   What will we do today?

3 Tomas answered,   We could read.

4 Tomas whispered,   Maybe the sun will come out soon.

5 Jan whined,   But what will we do now?

6 Tomas said,   Use your imagination!

Finish the sentence below. Use quotation marks to show what Jan asked.

Jan asked, _____

_____

Quotation Marks

Fill in the bubble next to the correct way to write the sentence.

1
- ○ Let's make a sand castle, said Lenny.
- ○ "Let's make a sand castle, said Lenny.
- ○ "Let's make a sand castle," said Lenny.

2
- ○ Where's the pail and shovel?" asked Sonya.
- ○ "Where's the pail and shovel?" asked Sonya.
- ○ Where's the pail and shovel? asked Sonya

3
- ○ Sara said, "Maybe Otis can help."
- ○ Sara said, Maybe Otis can help."
- ○ Sara said, "Maybe Otis can help.

4
- ○ Do you want to dig? asked Lenny.
- ○ "Do you want to dig? asked Lenny.
- ○ "Do you want to dig?" asked Lenny.

5
- ○ Sonya shouted, Get some water!
- ○ Sonya shouted, "Get some water!
- ○ Sonya shouted, "Get some water!"

6
- ○ Look what we made! cried the children.
- ○ "Look what we made!" cried the children.
- ○ Look what we made!" cried the children.

Contractions With *not*

*A **contraction** is two words made into one word. An apostrophe takes the place of the missing letter or letters. In a contraction, **not** becomes **n't**.*

Read each sentence. Underline the contraction. Write the two words the contraction is made from.

1 The little old man and little old woman aren't ready. _____

2 The Gingerbread Man doesn't want to be eaten. _____

3 They can't catch him. _____

4 They couldn't run fast enough. _____

5 He didn't come back. _____

6 The Gingerbread Man isn't afraid of the fox. _____

Draw a line to match each contraction to the two words it is made from.

7 hadn't   were not

8 don't   had not

9 weren't   do not

Contractions With *not*

A **contraction** *is two words made into one word. An apostrophe takes the place of the missing letter or letters. In a contraction,* **not** *becomes* **n't**.

Read each sentence. Write a contraction for the underlined words.

  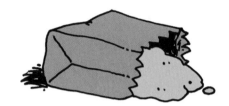

1 Cindy and Ed <u>could not</u> bake a cake. _____

2 There <u>was not</u> enough flour. _____

3 They <u>are not</u> happy. _____

4 They <u>cannot</u> surprise José. _____

5 <u>Do not</u> give up. _____

6 They <u>did not</u> give up.
They made cupcakes! _____

Write a sentence using a contraction you wrote.

_____

_____

Contractions With *not*

Fill in the bubble next to the contraction that correctly completes the sentence.

1 Our players ____ as big as theirs.
- ○ doesn't
- ○ haven't
- ○ aren't

2 Our coach ____ worried.
- ○ isn't
- ○ didn't
- ○ can't

3 They ____ run as fast as we can.
- ○ weren't
- ○ can't
- ○ wasn't

4 Their runner ____ tag first base.
- ○ doesn't
- ○ haven't
- ○ isn't

5 Their hitters ____ hit the ball hard.
- ○ isn't
- ○ weren't
- ○ don't

6 Our hitters ____ miss any balls.
- ○ doesn't
- ○ didn't
- ○ aren't

7 The other players ____ catch our balls.
- ○ couldn't
- ○ haven't
- ○ isn't

8 They ____ ready for us.
- ○ don't
- ○ hadn't
- ○ weren't

Subject/Verb Agreement

If the naming part of a sentence names one, add -s to the action word. If the naming part names more than one, do not add -s to the action word.

Read each sentence. Underline the word in parentheses ( ) that correctly completes it. Write the word on the line.

1 Kim _____ a story about a monkey. (write, writes)

2 The monkey _____ his friend in the city. (meet, meets)

3 The two friends _____ on the bus. (ride, rides)

4 The monkeys _____ for toys and presents. (shop, shops)

5 The store _____ at 7 o'clock. (close, closes)

6 The monkeys _____ the time. (forget, forgets)

7 The owner _____ the door. (lock, locks)

8 The friends _____ on the window. (bang, bangs)

9 Many people _____ for help. (call, calls)

10 Finally the monkeys _____ the door open. (hear, hears)

Subject/Verb Agreement

If the naming part of a sentence names one, add -s to the action word. If the naming part names more than one, do not add -s to the action word.

Read each sentence. Circle the action word in parentheses ( ) that correctly completes the sentence.

1 Two baby llamas (play/plays) in the mountains.

2 One baby llama (hide/hides) under a bush.

3 The baby animals (chase/chases) flying leaves.

4 Soon the mother llama (call/calls) them.

5 The babies (run/runs) to her.

6 The two babies (stand/stands) next to their mother.

7 One baby (close/closes) its eyes.

8 The mother llama (nudge/nudges) the baby gently.

9 But the baby llama (sleep/sleeps).

10 Soon both baby llamas (sleep/sleeps).

Subject/Verb Agreement

Fill in the bubble next to the word that correctly completes the sentence.

1 Two friends ____ beautiful bead necklaces.
○ make   ○ makes

2 One girl ____ some pieces of string.
○ cut   ○ cuts

3 The girls ____ red, blue, and yellow beads.
○ use   ○ uses

4 The yellow beads ____ in the dark.
○ glow   ○ glows

5 The necklaces ____ from the rod.
○ hang   ○ hangs

6 The boys ____ a necklace for their mother.
○ buy   ○ buys

7 One boy ____ the short necklace with round beads.
○ pick   ○ picks

8 The other boy ____ the necklace with square beads.
○ pick   ○ picks

9 Two sisters ____ the same red necklace.
○ wear   ○ wears

10 The girls ____ all the necklaces.
○ sell   ○ sells

More About Subject/Verb Agreement

If the naming part of a sentence is a noun or pronoun that names one, the verb ends in **s**, *except for the pronouns* **I** *and* **you**. *If the naming part is a noun or pronoun that names more than one, the verb does not end in* **-s**.

Read each sentence. Circle the correct verb to complete it.

1 John and his family (camp, camps) in the woods.

2 Alice (like, likes) hiking the best.

3 John (walk, walks) ahead of everyone.

4 Mom and John (build, builds) a campfire.

5 Dad and Alice (cook, cooks) dinner over the fire.

6 Alice and Mom (crawl, crawls) into the tent.

Choose two of the verbs you circled. Write a sentence using each verb.

_____

_____

© Scholastic Inc.

More About Subject/Verb Agreement

If the naming part of a sentence is a noun or pronoun that names one, the verb ends in **-s,** *except for the pronouns* **I** *and* **you***. If the naming part is a noun or pronoun that names more than one, the verb does not end in* **-s.**

Choose the correct action word from the box to complete each sentence. Write it on the line.

play	run	dive	climb	throw
plays	runs	dives	climbs	throws

1 Mia _____ ball with her friends.

2 The children like to _____ together.

3 Juan _____ faster than I do.

4 We _____ on a track team.

5 Tom and Kara _____ into the pool.

6 Mary _____ without her goggles.

7 They _____ very tall trees.

8 Liz _____ steep mountains.

9 Juan and Mia _____ balls.

10 I _____ the ball to Juan.

She hops.

They hop.

More About Subject/Verb Agreement

Fill in the bubble next to the verb that correctly completes the sentence.

1 Bobby ____ a sandwich for lunch.

○ bring   ○ brings

2 Maria ____ rice and black beans.

○ like   ○ likes

3 Bobby and Maria ____ lunches.

○ trade   ○ trades

4 The twins ____ fish sandwiches.

○ eat   ○ eats

5 The children ____ milk with their lunches.

○ drink   ○ drinks

6 They ____ fresh fruit for dessert.

○ buy   ○ buys

7 Jill ____ for a ripe, yellow banana.

○ ask   ○ asks

8 Aki ____ strawberries and blueberries.

○ want   ○ wants

9 Nathan ____ grapes on his tray.

○ put   ○ puts

10 Paulo and Sylvia ____ seats at the table.

○ find   ○ finds

Verbs *have, has, had*

*The verb **have** is irregular. Use **have** or **has** to tell about the present. Use **had** to tell about the past.*

Read each sentence. Write have, has, or had on the line in the sentence. Then write now or past on the line at the end to show if the sentence takes place now or in the past.

1 The man _____ many people in his restaurant last week.

_____

2 He _____ good food in his kitchen.

_____

3 Now the restaurant _____ ten tables.

_____

4 The boy _____ time to help his father today.

_____

5 The girl _____ time, too.

_____

6 The children _____ fun making salads and setting the tables today.

_____

7 They _____ a good time together in the restaurant.

_____

8 They _____ fun yesterday, too.

_____

Verbs *have, has, had*

*The verb **have** is irregular. Use **have** or **has** to tell about the present. Use **had** to tell about the past.*

Choose the correct word from the chart to complete each sentence.

In the Present	In the Past
have, has	had

1 Joe _____ new running shoes.

2 I _____ new shoes, too.

3 Last week we _____ old shoes.

4 I _____ a green shirt on.

5 Joe _____ a blue shirt on.

6 Yesterday we both _____ red shirts on.

7 Last year we _____ to walk to the park.

8 Now, I _____ skates.

9 Now, Joe _____ a bike.

Verbs *have, has, had*

Read each sentence. If the underlined word is correct, fill in the last bubble. If not, fill in the bubble next to the correct word.

1 I <u>have</u> a pet bird.

⚬ has   ⚬ had   ⚬ correct as is

2 Now, she <u>had</u> big white wings.

⚬ has   ⚬ have   ⚬ correct as is

3 Before, she <u>has</u> little white wings.

⚬ have   ⚬ had   ⚬ correct as is

4 The baby bird <u>have</u> closed eyes when it was born.

⚬ has   ⚬ had   ⚬ correct as is

5 Now the baby bird <u>had</u> open eyes.

⚬ has   ⚬ have   ⚬ correct as is

6 The mother and baby birds <u>had</u> fun now.

⚬ has   ⚬ have   ⚬ correct as is

7 The baby bird <u>has</u> little wings now.

⚬ have   ⚬ had   ⚬ correct as is

8 It <u>had</u> even smaller wings when it was born.

⚬ has   ⚬ have   ⚬ correct as is

© Scholastic Inc.

Scholastic Success With

WRITING

You're Sharp!

 A sentence begins with a **capital letter.**

Circle the words that show the correct way to begin each sentence.

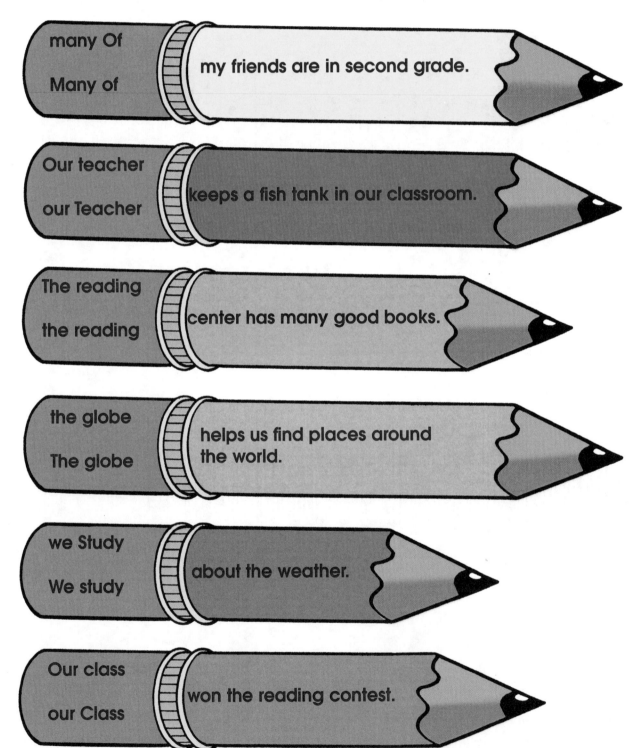

many Of

Many of

my friends are in second grade.

Our teacher

our Teacher

keeps a fish tank in our classroom.

The reading

the reading

center has many good books.

the globe

The globe

helps us find places around
the world.

we Study

We study

about the weather.

Our class

our Class

won the reading contest.

Stick With It

 A sentence begins with a **capital letter**.

Write the beginning words correctly to make a sentence.

1.  art class _____ begins at noon.

2. today we _____ are making clay pots.

3. first, we _____ form the clay into balls.

4.  the next _____ step is to make a hole in the ball.

5. my teacher _____ dries the pots.

6.  next week _____ we will paint the pots.

A Whale of a Sentence

 A **telling sentence** *ends with a* **period** *(.)*.

Rewrite the sentences using capital letters and periods.

1. the blue whale is the largest animal in the world

2. even dinosaurs were not as large as the blue whale

3. blue whales are not part of the fish family

_____

4. the blue whale has no teeth

_____

5. blue whales eat tiny sea creatures

6. blue whales have two blowholes

That Sounds Fishy to Me

 *A **telling sentence** begins with a **capital letter** and ends with a **period**.*

Write a sentence about each fish. Remember to tell a complete idea.

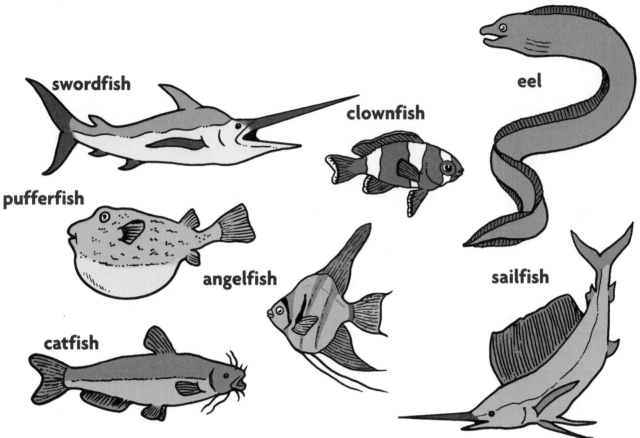

swordfish

eel

clownfish

pufferfish

angelfish

sailfish

catfish

1. The swordfish has a long snout.

2. _____

3. _____

4. _____

5. _____

6. _____

7. _____

Ask Mother Goose

*A sentence that asks a question ends with a **question mark** (?).*
It often begins with one of these words.

Who . . .	*Where . . .*	*Why . . .*	*Could . . .*
What . . .	*When . . .*	*Will . . .*	

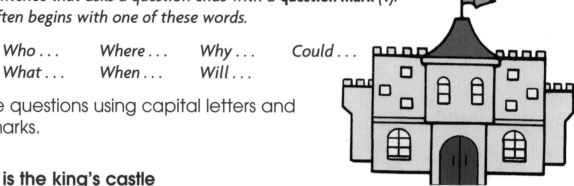

Rewrite the questions using capital letters and question marks.

1. where is the king's castle

_____

2. who helped Humpty Dumpty

_____

3. why did the cow jump over the moon

_____

4. will the frog become a prince

_____

5. could the three mice see

_____

Ask the Wolf

 An **asking sentence** *begins with a* **capital letter** *and ends with a* **question mark** *(?).*
It often begins with one of these words.

| How . . . | Can . . . | Would . . . |
| Did . . . | Is . . . | Should . . . |

Imagine that you can meet the Big Bad Wolf. What questions would you ask him about Little Red Riding Hood and the Three Little Pigs? Use a different beginning word for each question you write.

1. How _____

2. Did _____

3. Can _____

1. Is _____

2. Should _____

3. Would _____

 Pretend that you are the Big Bad Wolf. Write a sentence on another piece of paper to answer each question above.

Is Your Head in the Clouds?

 A **telling sentence** *ends with a* **period** *(.).*
An **asking sentence** *ends with a* **question mark** *(?).*

Finish each sentence by putting a period or a question mark in the cloud at the end.

1. **Clouds can look like cotton balls, feathers, or blankets**

2. **Do you know what makes a cloud form in the sky**

3. **Have you ever seen dark clouds on rainy days**

4. **Dark clouds may bring thunderstorms**

5. **Can you imagine pictures in the clouds**

6. **White clouds drift across the blue sky**

7. **Why don't we see clouds every day**

8. **Rain, snow, sleet, and hail may fall from clouds**

 Find two telling sentences and two questions in one of your favorite books. Write them on another piece of paper.

© Scholastic Inc.

Sunny Sentences

Every sentence begins with a **capital letter**.
A **telling sentence** *ends with a* **period** *(.)*.
An **asking sentence** *ends with a* **question mark** *(?)*.

Rewrite each sentence correctly.

1. the sun is the closest star to Earth

_____

2. the sun is not the brightest star

_____

3. what is the temperature of the sun

_____

4. the sun is a ball of hot gas

_____

5. how large is the sun

_____

6. will the sun ever burn out

_____

On another piece of paper, write a sentence with two mistakes. Ask a friend to circle the mistakes.

© Scholastic Inc.

Camp Fiddlestick

 A telling sentence is called a **statement**. *An asking sentence is called a* **question**.
Now ask yourself:

How do sentences begin? How do statements end? How do questions end?

Write three statements and three questions about the picture.

Statements:

1. _____

2. _____

3. _____

Questions:

1. _____

2. _____

3. _____

 **Sing "Where is Thumbkin?" to yourself. Count the number of questions and statements in
the song.**

A Happy Camper

Complete:
Every sentence begins with a _____ .
A statement ends with a _____ .
A question ends with a _____ .

Uh oh! Dalton was in a hurry when he wrote this letter. Help him find 10 mistakes. Circle them.

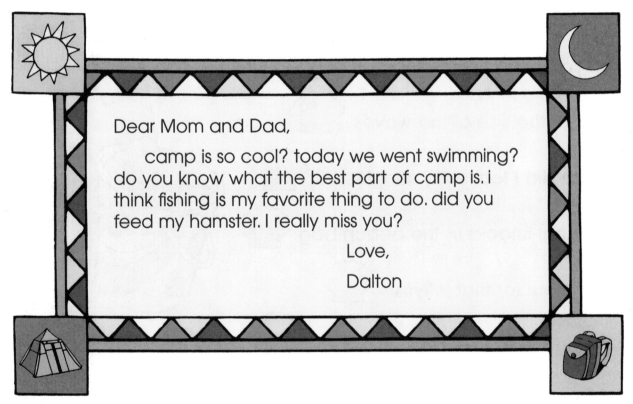

Dear Mom and Dad,

camp is so cool? today we went swimming? do you know what the best part of camp is. i think fishing is my favorite thing to do. did you feed my hamster. I really miss you?

Love,

Dalton

Now choose two questions and two statements from Dalton's letter. Rewrite each correctly.

1. _____

2. _____

3. _____

4. _____

 On another piece of paper, write a letter to a friend or family member. Include two statements and two questions.

A Day at the Beach

 A sentence that shows strong feeling or excitement is called an **exclamation**. *It ends with an* **exclamation point** *(!). For example: Look at that shark!*

Finish each sentence by putting a period, a question mark, or an exclamation point in the shell at the end.

1. I wonder if Jamie will be at the beach today

2. Did you bring the beach ball

3. Look at the size of the waves

4. Where did I leave my sunglasses

5. Mom put snacks in the beach bag

6. Watch out for that jellyfish

7. Do you want to build a sandcastle

8. The sun is bright today

9. Did you see that sailboat

10. Don't step on that starfish

11. It is windy near the seashore

12. Should we put up an umbrella

Read these sentences: I see a sand crab. I see a sand crab! How does your voice change?

© Scholastic Inc.

Seashore Sentences

Complete:

A _____ *ends with a period.*

A _____ *ends with a question mark.*

An _____ *ends with an exclamation point.*

Write a statement (S), a question (Q), and an exclamation (E) about each picture.

S _____

_____

Q _____

_____

E _____

_____

S _____

_____

Q _____

_____

E _____

_____

On another piece of paper, write a statement, a question, and an exclamation about a cartoon in the newspaper.

Building Blocks

 *A good sentence has a part that tells who or what the sentence is about. This is called the **subject**.*

Make a list of possible subjects to complete each sentence.

_____ jumped the fence.

1. _____
2. _____
3. _____

_____ is too full.

1. _____
2. _____
3. _____

 *A good sentence has a part that tells what happens. This is called the **action**.*

Make a list of possible actions to complete each sentence.

We _____ on the playground.

1. _____
2. _____
3. _____

The cowboy _____ on his horse.

1. _____
2. _____
3. _____

 On another piece of paper, make a list of five subjects you would like to write about.

© Scholastic Inc.

Keep Building!

 Some sentences have a part that tells where or when the action is happening.

For each sentence, make a list of possible endings that tell where or when the action happens.

The wind blew _____.

1. _____

2. _____

3. _____

The baby tripped _____.

1. _____

2. _____

3. _____

Complete each sentence.

1. _____ made us laugh
   last night.

2. The door leads _____.

3. The crowd _____
   at the circus.

4. The paint bucket spilled _____.

5. _____ was never
   seen again.

6. The firefighter _____ into the
   fire truck.

Get Your Ticket!

Write a sentence to match each picture. Be sure to include a subject, an action, and a part that tells where or when.

1. A boy climbs a tree in his backyard.

2. _____

3. _____

 Find a cartoon in the newspaper. Use the pictures to write a sentence on another piece of paper. Be sure to include a subject, an action, and a part that tells where or when.

Slide Show

 A sentence is more interesting when it includes a subject, an action, and a part that tells where or when.

Write three sentences and draw pictures to match.

subject	action	where or when

1. _____

subject	action	where or when

2. _____

subject	action	where or when

3. _____

 Switch the sentence parts around to make three silly sentences! Write the sentences on another piece of paper.

Mystery Bags

 Describing words *help you imagine how something looks, feels, smells, sounds, or tastes.*

Make a list of words that describe the object in each bag below.

 Use a paper sack to make a real mystery bag. Place an object in the bag and give describing clues to someone at home. Can he or she guess the mystery object?

180   Scholastic Success With 2nd Grade

© Scholastic Inc.

What Does It Feel Like?

 Describing words *often provide information about something that we can discover with our senses.*

Choose the best describing word to complete the sentence.

1. Cotton candy is _____.

2. Before it is cooked, a potato is _____.

3. A peach's skin is _____.

4. A needle is _____.

5. Mashed potatoes are _____.

Word Bank

thin

soft

fluffy

fuzzy

hard

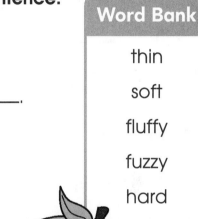

Look at the words in the Word Bank.
Find and circle each word in the word search.

C	T	R	O	U	G	H
S	H	I	N	Y	B	H
M	S	J	O	W	U	V
O	S	H	Y	B	M	L
O	W	J	Q	B	P	I
T	H	I	C	K	Y	A
H	S	T	I	C	K	Y

Word Bank

thick

bumpy

rough

sticky

smooth

shiny

Country Roads

 A good sentence uses describing words to help the reader "paint a picture" in his or her mind.

Add a describing word from the list to finish each sentence.

1. The _____ chicken laid
   _____ eggs in her nest.

2. The _____ barn
   keeps the _____
   animals warm at night.

3. _____ carrots grow in
   the _____ garden.

4. Two _____ pigs sleep in
   the _____ pen.

5. The _____ cows drink
   from the _____ pond.

6. A _____ scarecrow
   frightens the _____ birds.

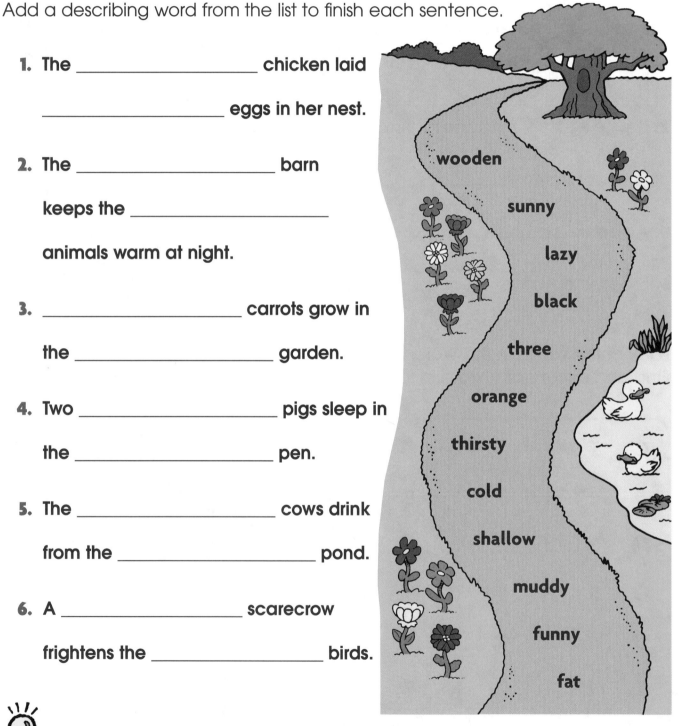

wooden

sunny

lazy

black

three

orange

thirsty

cold

shallow

muddy

funny

fat

© Scholastic Inc.

 On another piece of paper, write three sentences describing your favorite place to visit.

It's in the Bag

 Describing words *make a sentence more interesting.*

Add a describing word to each sentence.

1. My friend's _____ dog has fleas!

2. The _____ popcorn is in the big bowl.

3. How did the _____ worm get on the sidewalk?

4. The _____ ocean waves crashed against the rocks.

5. The _____ ball broke a window at school!

6. My _____ skin itched from poison ivy.

7. The two _____ squirrels chased each other up the tree.

8. The _____ sand felt good on my feet.

9. Are the _____ apples ready to be picked?

10. The _____ ball was hard to catch.

11. Is the _____ salamander hiding under the rock?

12. The _____ snow cone melted quickly.

Ask someone at home to make a mystery bag and give you clues about the object inside.

© Scholastic Inc.

City Streets

 A good sentence uses describing words.

Write a statement (S), a question (Q), and an exclamation (E) about the picture. Use each of the following describing words:

fast   **busy**   **crowded**

S _____

_____

Q _____

_____

E _____

_____

 Describe a "mystery object" to a friend. Can he or she guess what you are describing?

Football Frenzy

 A sentence is more interesting when it gives exact information.

Replace each word to make the sentence more exact.

1. The  ball game starts soon.

   The ___soccer___ game starts ___now___.

2. We are meeting  her 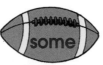 there.

   We are meeting _____ _____.

3. Let's eat 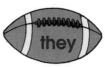 this and  that before the game.

   Let's eat _____ and _____ before

   the game.

4. I hope  they score  some points.

   I hope _____ score _____ points.

5.   They were also there.

   _____ were also _____.

6.   He played a good game!

   _____ played a _____ game!

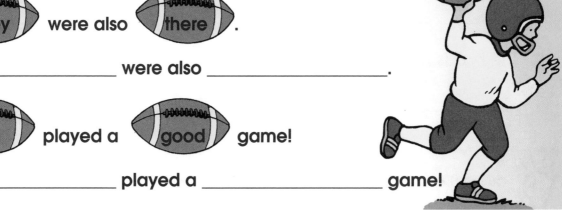

Take Me Out to the Ball Game

 A sentence is more interesting when it gives complete information.

Finish each sentence so that it answers the  question.

1. The players get to the stadium  when

_____

2. The team is excited because  why

_____

3. The fans arrive in  what

_____

4. Flags are flying  where

_____

5. A man sings the "Star-Spangled Banner"  when

_____

6. The fans cheer for  whom

_____

7. The ball is hit  where

_____

 On another piece of paper, write a sentence about your favorite game. Be sure to tell who plays the game with you.

Cake and Ice Cream

  *Two sentences that share the same subject can be combined to make one sentence by using the word **and**.*

Rewrite the sentences by combining their endings.

1. **The party was fun.**
   The party was exciting.

   <u>The party was fun and exciting.</u>

2. **We blew up orange balloons.**
   We blew up red balloons.

   _____

3. **We ate cake.**
   We ate ice cream.

   _____

4. **The cake frosting was green.**
   The cake frosting was yellow.

   _____

5. **We made a bookmark.**
   We made a clay pot.

   _____

6. **We brought games.**
   We brought prizes.

   _____

Salt and Pepper

Two sentences that share the same ending can also be combined to make one sentence.

Rewrite the sentences by combining their subjects.

1. These peanuts are salty!
   These pretzels are salty!

   These peanuts and pretzels are salty!

2. The first graders eat lunch at noon.
   The second graders eat lunch at noon.

   _____

3. Where is the salt?
   Where is the pepper?

   _____

4. The napkins are on the table.
   The forks are on the table.

   _____

5. Are the muffins in the oven?
   Are the cookies in the oven?

   _____

6. Michael bought lunch today.
   Stephen bought lunch today.

   _____

Great Gardening Tips

 Sentences can also be combined to make them more interesting. Key words can help put two sentences together.

I will plan my garden. I am waiting for spring.

I will plan my garden while I am waiting for spring.

Combine the two sentences using the key word. Write a new sentence.

1. Fill a cup with water. Add some flower seeds.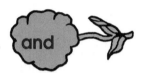

_____

2. This will soften the seeds. They are hard.

_____

3. Fill a cup with dirt. The seeds soak in water.

_____

4. Bury the seeds in the cup. The dirt covers them.

_____

5. Add water to the plant. Do not add too much.

_____

6. Set the cup in the sun. The plant will grow.

_____

Growing Sentences

 Sentences can be combined to make them more interesting.

Write a combined sentence of your own. Use the given key word to help you.

1. while I watch TV while my mom makes
lunch,

2. until _____

_____

3. because _____

_____

4. but _____

_____

5. or _____

_____

6. and _____

_____

 On another piece of paper, write a combined sentence of your own using one of these key words: *after, before, during.*

The Sky's the Limit

Some sentences include a list. A **comma** *(,) is used to separate each item in the list.*

For example: Mrs. Jones asked the class to work on pages two, three, and four.

Fill in the blanks to make a list in each sentence. Watch for commas!

1. I ate _____, _____,

    and _____ for breakfast.

2. We stayed with Grandma on _____,

    _____, and _____ nights.

3. I found _____, _____,

    and _____ in my party bag.

4. The boys played _____,

    _____, and _____

    at summer camp.

5. The _____, _____,

    and _____ ate the corn we scattered.

6. The pigs built their houses using _____,

    _____, and _____

 Cut a balloon out of paper. On one side, list
three objects that fly. On the other side,
write a sentence that lists these objects.

Up, Up, and Away

*Some sentences include a list. A **comma** (,) is used to separate each item in the list.*

Write a sentence that includes a list of the words that are given.

coat
hat
gloves

1. _____

_____

spelling
reading
math

2. _____

_____

bread
peanut butter
jelly

3. _____

_____

birds
flowers
butterflies

4. _____

_____

On another piece of paper, write a sentence that lists colors or shapes of balloons.

© Scholastic Inc.

Out of This World

After you write a sentence, go back and look for mistakes. This is called **proofreading** *your work.*

Use the proofreading marks to correct the two mistakes in each sentence.

<u>mars</u> = Make a capital letter.   (?) = Add a question mark.   (!) = Add an exclamation point.

(.) = Add a period.   (,) = Add a comma.   [   ] = Add a word. (Write a describing word in the box.)

1. Sometimes I can see mars Jupiter, and Saturn with my telescope.

[   ]

2. There are ∧ stars in our galaxy

[   ]

3. comets are ∧ pieces of ice and rock.

[   ]

4. The sun is really a ∧ star

5. is there life on any other planet

[   ]

6. Look at that ∧ shooting star

7. can you imagine traveling in space

[   ]

8. i think I saw a ∧ alien.

 On another piece of paper, write two sentences about space with two mistakes in each. Ask someone at home to proofread your sentences. Is he or she correct?

Smart About Saturn

 Be sure to proofread your work.

Matthew's science report has nine mistakes. Use proofreading marks to correct his work. Then rewrite the report. Add at least two describing words to the report.

Saturn
by Matthew

Saturn is famous for the rings that surround it? its rings are made of ice, rock and dirt. The rings circle around the planet! Saturn is made mostly of gas? saturn's gases are lighter than water That means Saturn would float if you put it into a tub of water Saturn has more than 60 moons

_____

_____

_____

_____

_____

 On another piece of paper, write a short report about your favorite planet. Be sure to proofread it when you are done.

Banana-Rama

Color the word that is missing from each sentence.

1. We _____ a spelling test yesterday.　taked　took

2. There _____ frost on the ground.　was　were

3. Tommy _____ the Statue of Liberty.　seen　saw

4. How _____ elephants are at the zoo?　much　many

5. Claire _____ her lizard to school.　brought　brang

6. Have you _____ my dog?　seen　saw

7. Alyssa _____ a new pair of skates.　gots　has

8. You _____ supposed to finish your work.　are　is

9. We _____ standing near a snake!　were　was

10. They _____ a pig in the mud.　seen　saw

11. We _____ our winter boots.　wore　weared

12. Is she _____ to come over?　gonna　going

13. _____ your cat climb trees?　Do　Does

14. Rosie _____ cookies to the bake sale.　brang　brought

An Apple a Day

Find the word that is incorrect in each sentence. Draw an apple around it and write the correct word on the line.

1. Laura brang a snack to camp. _____

2. I seen the sea lion show at the zoo. _____

3. Drew gots a dinosaur collection. _____

4. Mara taked her dog for a walk. _____

5. We is going to see the movie. _____

6. Jason runned to the playground. _____

7. How many pennies do you got? _____

8. The kids was having fun. _____

9. Did you saw the soccer game? _____

10. How much do that cost? _____

11. Kelly brang her cat to school! _____

12. I does my homework after school. _____

 Eat an apple. Then on another piece of paper, write a statement, a question, and an exclamation describing the apple. Be sure each sentence uses correct words.

© Scholastic Inc.

Stories of Nature

 Sentences should be written in the correct order to tell a story.

Finish the stories by writing a sentence about each of the last two pictures.

First: Two birds build a nest.

Next: _____

Last: _____

First: A flower bud grows.

Next: _____

Last: _____

Nestled in a Nest

Write a sentence about each picture to make your own story.

_____

_____

_____

_____

_____

_____

_____

_____

_____

_____

_____

_____

 Read your story to a friend.

Stories on Parade

 *Stories have a **beginning** (B), a **middle** (M), and an **end** (E).*

Write a middle sentence that tells what happens next. Then write an ending sentence that tells what happens last.

 **B** During the parade, five funny clowns jumped out of a purple bus.

M Next, _____

E Last, _____

 B A big balloon got loose in the wind.

 M Next, _____

E Last, _____

 B A group of horses stopped right in front of us.

M Next, _____

 **E** Last, _____

 **B** Some clowns were riding motorcycles.

M Next, _____

E Last, _____

 On another piece of paper, draw a picture of a parade that shows what is happening in the stories you wrote.

© Scholastic Inc.

An Original Story

Choose a story idea from the list. Then write a beginning, middle, and ending sentence to make a story of your own. Color a picture to match each part.

The Best Birthday Ever	**King for a Day**
My Dog's Dream	**The Magic Rock**

First: _____

_____

_____

_____

Next: _____

_____

_____

_____

Last: _____

_____

_____

_____

Staple three pieces of paper together to make a book. Write another story and draw a picture for each part.

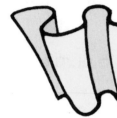

© Scholastic Inc.

Once Upon a Time

 *The **setting** of a story tells when or where it is happening.*

Imagine that you are writing a story for each picture below. How will you describe the setting? Write a sentence describing each setting.

setting	→	characters	→	problem	→	solution

It was a hot morning in the desert.

 On another piece of paper, describe the setting of your favorite movie.

All Kinds of Characters

 The people or animals in a story are called **characters**.

Some characters are likable and others are not. Write a describing sentence about each character. Be sure to give each character a name.

| setting | → | characters | → | problem | → | solution |

_____

_____

_____

_____

_____

_____

_____

_____

_____

 On another piece of paper, make a list of four people you know well. Write three words that describe each of them. Cross out the four names and write animal names instead. Now you have four characters to use in your next story!

That's a Problem!

*To make a story exciting, one of the characters often runs into a **problem.***

Think about each character in the sentences below. What could happen that would make a problem for that character? Write the next sentence creating a problem.

setting ⟶ characters ⟶ problem ⟶ solution

1. Beauty Butterfly was enjoying the warm spring day.

_____

2. Jesse was supposed to wear shoes outside.

_____

3. Gabby could not wait to bite into her apple.

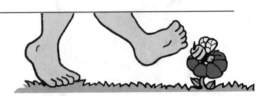

_____

4. Ben smacked the baseball into the air.

_____

5. Barney Bass had never seen such a big worm!

_____

Good Solution!

*At the end of a story, the problem is usually solved. This is called the **solution**.*

Read the beginning and middle parts of the stories below. Write an ending solution for each.

setting → characters → problem → solution

David and his dog, Spot, were best friends. They went everywhere together. At bedtime, David whistled for Spot to jump in his bed. One winter night, David whistled and whistled, but Spot did not come.

_____

_____

_____

Josh loved second grade, but he did not like recess. Josh's class was always the last one out to the playground. Every day, Josh ran to get a swing, but they were always taken.

_____

_____

_____

On another piece of paper, make a list of three problems you have faced. How did you solve each problem?

The Mighty Knight

 A **story map** *helps you plan the setting, characters, problem, and solution.*

Write a sentence about each part of the map to make a story.

_____

_____

_____

_____

_____

_____

_____

_____

 Read your story to a friend.

A Story Fit for a King

 Use a story map to help plan your story before you begin writing.

Complete the map. Then use it to write a story "fit for a king."

_____

_____

_____

_____

_____

_____

_____

_____

 Turn your story into a puppet show! Perform your puppet show for someone at home.

The Father of Our Country

 After you finish writing, go back and look for mistakes.

Use the proofreading marks to correct eight mistakes in the letter.

mars = **Make a capital letter.**   ? = **Add a question mark.**   ! = **Add an exclamation point.**

• = **Add a period.**   , = **Add a comma.**

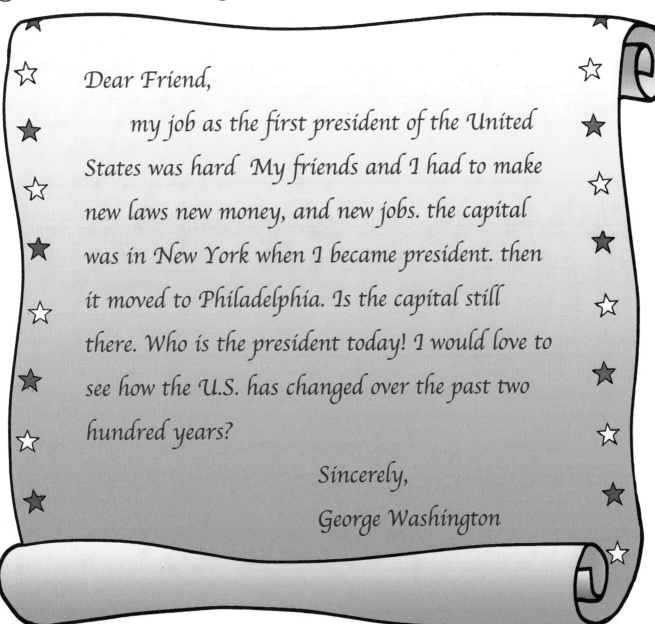

Dear Friend,

   my job as the first president of the United States was hard My friends and I had to make new laws new money, and new jobs. the capital was in New York when I became president. then it moved to Philadelphia. Is the capital still there. Who is the president today! I would love to see how the U.S. has changed over the past two hundred years?

Sincerely,

George Washington

 On another piece of paper, write a letter to today's president. The White House address is: 1600 Pennsylvania Avenue Washington, D.C. 20500.

Presidential Pen Pals

*A **friendly letter** has five parts: the date, greeting, body, closing, and signature.*

Use the five parts to write a letter back to George Washington. Be sure to proofread your work for mistakes.

_____
(today's date)

_____,
(greeting)

_____
(body)
_____
_____
_____
_____
_____
_____
_____

_____,
(closing)

_____
(your name)

Scholastic Success With

MAPS

Looking at a map

Looking at a Map

Have you ever been in an airplane? Did you look down on Earth? Then you know that things look different from above.

This photo was taken from an airplane. It shows a community.

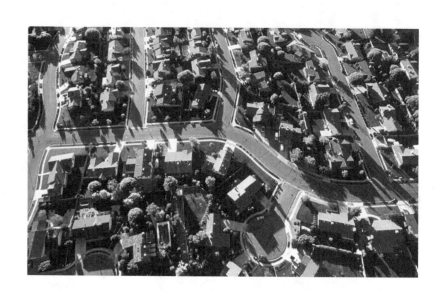

Circle YES if you see the thing in the photo.

Circle NO if you do not.

1. building   (YES)   NO

2. street   (YES)   NO

3. car   YES   (NO)

4. bus   YES   (NO)

5. What else do you see? _tres_____

210   Scholastic Success With 2nd Grade

© Scholastic Inc.

The map on this page shows the same place as the photo.
A **map** is a drawing of a place from above. A map shows
where things are.

10010

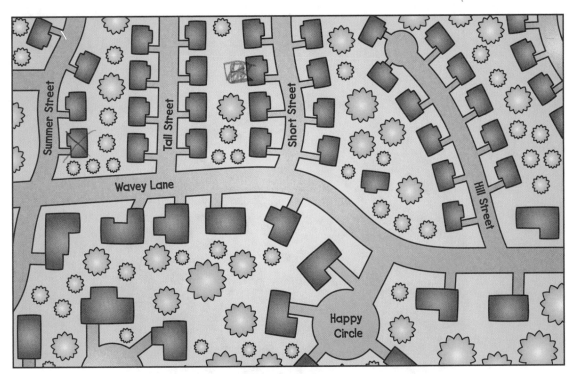

1. **Find the house on the corner of Summer Street and
   Wavey Lane on the map. Make an X on that house.**

2. **Find a swimming pool in the photo.
   Draw it in the same place on the map.**

3. **How are the map and photo alike?** _texe befe_
   seutte s.

4. **How are the map and photo different?** _Photo_
   seaerrele six

A Globe and Earth

Pretend you are in a spaceship. You look out and see a planet. It is Earth, your home. This photo shows what Earth looks like from space. Isn't it beautiful?

1. **You can see only one side of Earth at a time.**

   What shape is Earth? _____

2. **Does Earth have more land or water?** _____

3. **Why is part of Earth green?** _____

Have you ever played with a toy car? A toy car is a model of a real car. This picture shows a **globe**. A globe is a model of Earth. You can see that the globe and Earth are the same shape.

1. What shape is a globe? _____

2. Is the globe bigger or smaller than Earth? _____

3. What do the words on the globe tell you? _____

_____

A World Map

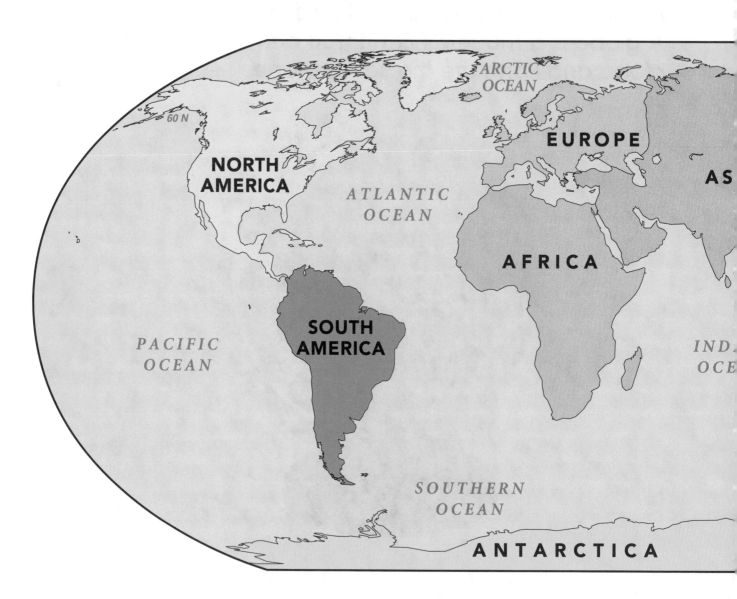

A globe is handy for finding places on Earth.
A world map can show all of Earth, too.

1. This map shows Earth's continents. A **continent** is a large body
   of land. Can you find all seven of Earth's continents? Write an
   X on each one.

PACIFIC
OCEAN

AUSTRALIA

2. The map also shows Earth's oceans.

   An ocean is a large body of salt water.

   How many oceans do you see?

   _____

3. Name four continents that begin with "A."

   _____

   _____

   _____

   _____

4. Name two oceans that begin with "A."

   _____

   _____

5. How is a world map different from a globe?

   _____

   _____

A Compass Rose

This is a **compass rose**. A compass rose is a symbol that helps you read a map. The arrows on a compass rose point to the four main **directions**. They are north, south, east, and west.

North is the direction toward the North Pole.

South is the direction toward the South Pole.

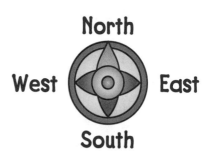

When you face north, west is on the left. East is on the right.

Sometimes a compass rose has letters that stand for the direction words.

1. **N stands for** _____

2. **S stands for** _____

3. **E stands for** _____

4. **W stands for** _____

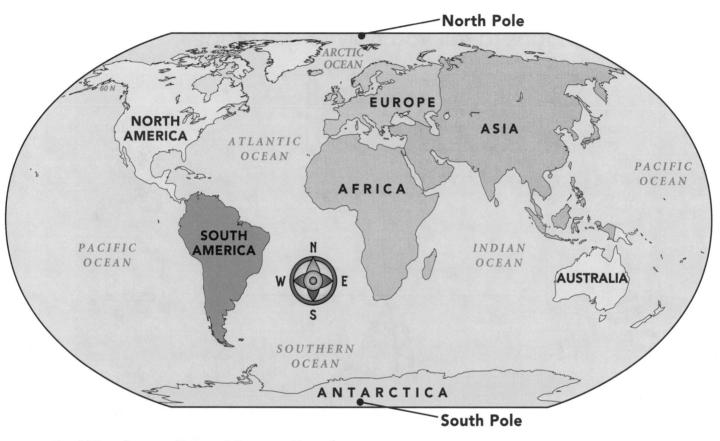

1. What continent is south of
   South America and Africa? _____

2. What ocean is north of
   North America and Europe? _____

3. Draw a straight line from the North Pole to the South Pole.
   Are these places east or west of your line?

   Indian Ocean _____   North America _____

   Europe _____   Australia _____

Using Directions

When you use a map, look for the compass rose.
Use the directions to tell you how to get places.

Pretend you are at this park. Use a pencil to trace the way you go.

1. Start at the gate and go east. What do you see? _____

2. Go to the swings. In which direction are they? _____

3. Next you come to a fountain.
   In which direction did you walk? _____

4. If you go north, what will you see? _____

Lucy lives in Fun City. Her house is on Chuckles Street. Find Lucy's house.

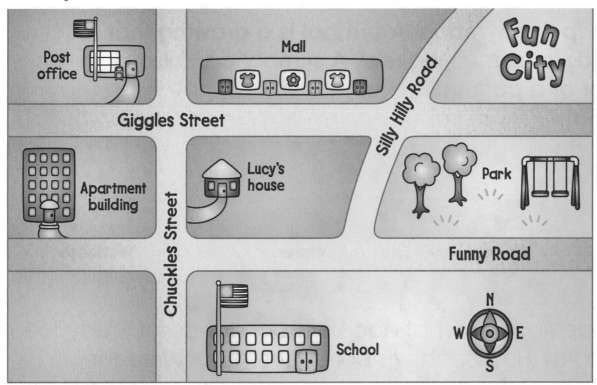

Circle the correct answers.

1. **To get to the park, Lucy goes** _____.
   west   east   south

2. **The mall is** _____ **of Lucy's house.**
   north   south   west

3. **The post office is** _____ **of the mall.**
   south   east   west

4. **When Lucy walks to school, she heads** _____.
   north   west   south

5. **If Lucy walks west on Funny Road, she will be at the** _____.
   park   library   apartment building

Map Symbols

A map has **symbols**. A symbol is a drawing that stands for something real. A symbol can also be a color or a pattern.

Woods   **Water**   **Wetlands**

A map key tells what each symbol stands for. Study the map key. Find each symbol on the map. Write the number of the symbol in the correct circle on the map.

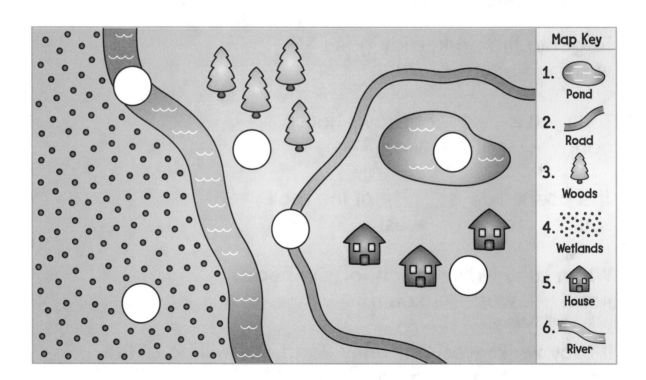

© Scholastic Inc.

Use the map key and the compass rose to answer
the questions.

1. What does the symbol mean? _____

2. What street is north of the school? _____

3. What is just west of the factory? _____

4. What color is used to show the park? _____

5. Is the park north or south of the houses? _____

Using Map Symbols

Welcome to the zoo! You can use this map to get around.

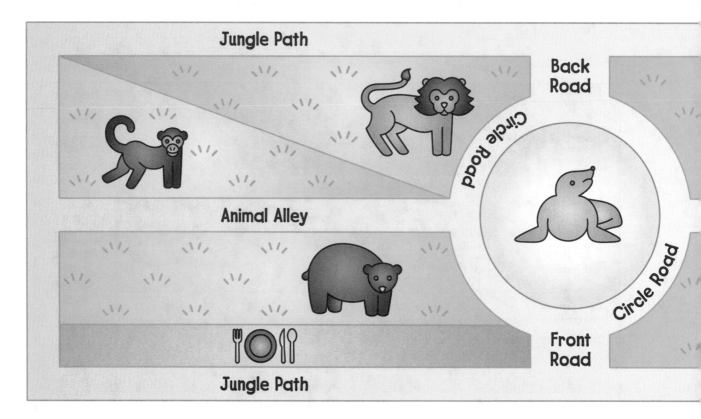

Most zoos have maps for visitors to use.
Use the map to answer the questions.

1. What does this symbol mean? _____

2. Are the elephants on the
   east or west side of the zoo? _____

3. Can you get a snack at this zoo? _____

4. Are the monkeys north or south of the bears? _____

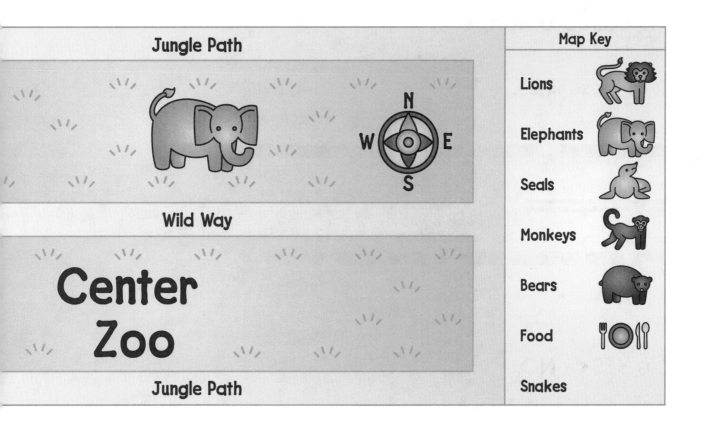

5. On what road are the seals? _____

6. Does this zoo have lions? _____

7. Does this zoo have hippos? _____

8. The map key is missing a snake symbol.
   Draw a snake symbol in the map key.

9. Find the space south of the elephants.
   Add your snake symbol there.

Distance

A map can show how far it is from one place to another. This is called **distance**.

Look at these lines.

A.

B.

C.

Circle YES or **NO**.

1. Line A is the longest line.   YES   NO

2. Line C is the shortest line.   YES   NO

3. Line B is longer than Line C.   YES   NO

4. Line C is longer than Line A.   YES   NO

5. Line B is shorter than Line A.   YES   NO

6. Line C is longer than Line B.   YES   NO

The Tang family is playing catch.
This map shows where each player is standing.

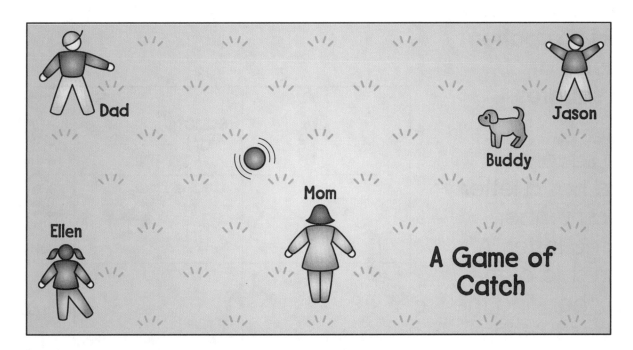

Use a ruler to help answer the questions.

1. The longest distance is between Ellen and_____.

2. The shortest distance is between Jason and_____.

3. Is Buddy farther from Mom or Ellen? _____.

4. Is Dad nearer to Mom or Buddy? _____.

5. It is almost the same distance between
   Ellen and Mom and Mom and_____.

A Map Grid

Some maps have lines like this:
These lines form a **grid**.
A grid is a pattern
of lines that
form squares.

Each square on
a grid has a letter
and a number.
Find the letter "A"
at the side of the
map. Then find the
number 1 at the
top of the map.
The first square
in the top row is A1.
Can you find A2?

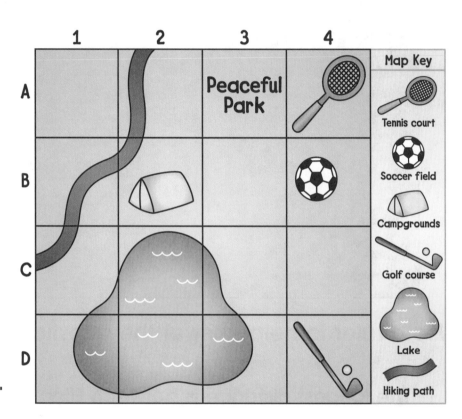

Use the grid to answer the questions.

1. **What is in A4?** _____

2. **In what square is the soccer field?** _____

3. **Find D4. What can you do there?** _____

4. **Through what squares does the hiking path go?** _____

Here is a map grid game you can play. Study the map. Then look for each square below. Write the square name under each picture.

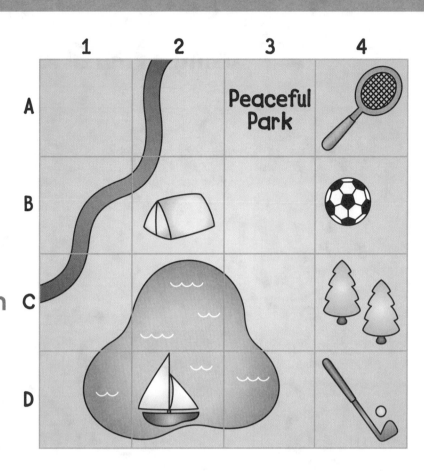

1.

_____

2.

_____

3.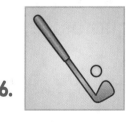

_____

4.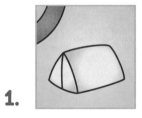

_____

5.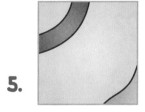

_____

6.

_____

Using a Map Grid

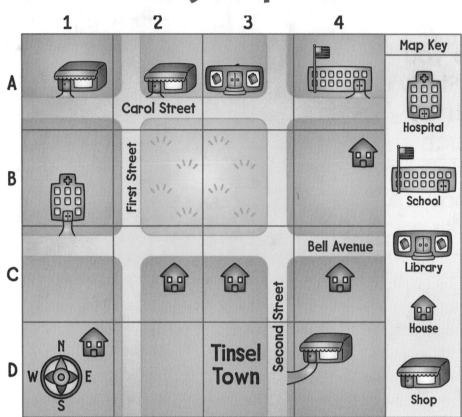

A grid helps you find places on a map. Use the grid to answer the questions.

1. In which square is the hospital? _____

2. What is in square C4? _____

3. What street runs through squares A2, B2, C2, and D2? _____

4. Can you shop in D1? _____

5. You want to borrow a book. In which square would you look? _____

This map shows the state of Ohio.

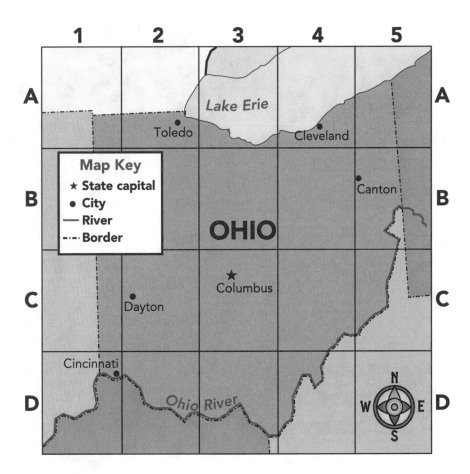

Use the grid and map key to answer the questions.

1. In what square is Cleveland? _____

2. What city is in D1? _____

3. What is in A3? _____

4. In what square is Columbus? _____

5. Name the squares that the
   Ohio River runs through. _____

The United States

This is a map of the
United States.

The map shows the 50 states.
It also shows the capital of each
state. A capital is a city where
government leaders work.

The United States
has a capital, too.
It is Washington, D.C.

Find this symbol ————
on the map. A border shows where
places begin and end. The borders
on this map show the dividing lines
between states.

1. **Find your state on
   the map. What is the
   capital of your state?**_____

2. **Find Oregon.
   What is its capital?**_____

3. **Find Texas. What is its capital?**_____

4. **Is Washington, D.C., in the east
   or west part of the country?**_____

© Scholastic Inc.

MAP KEY

——	State border
⊛	National capital
★	State capital

5. Find Montana. What state has a border on the west side of Montana? _____

6. Find your state. How many states share a border with it? _____

Looking at a State

Have you ever been to Nebraska?
This is how Nebraska looks on a map.

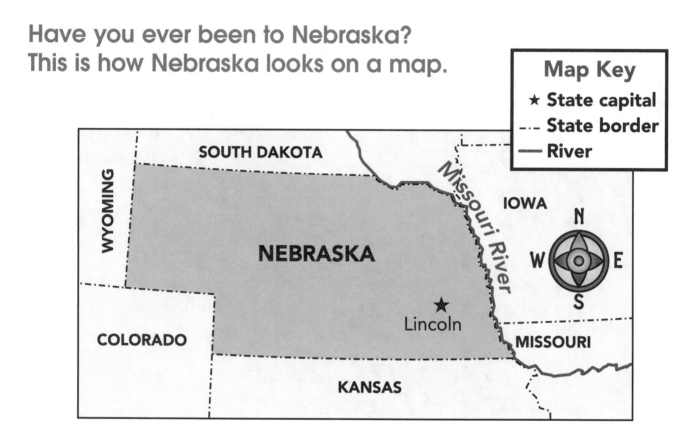

Map Key
★ State capital
-··- State border
— River

Use the map to answer the questions.

1. What is the symbol for the state capital? _____

2. What is the capital of Nebraska? _____

3. What state is north of Nebraska? _____

4. What states are on the
   western border of Nebraska? _____

5. What forms the border
   between Nebraska and Iowa? _____

The grid can help you find places in Nebraska.

Map Key
★ State capital
● City
-·- State border
— River

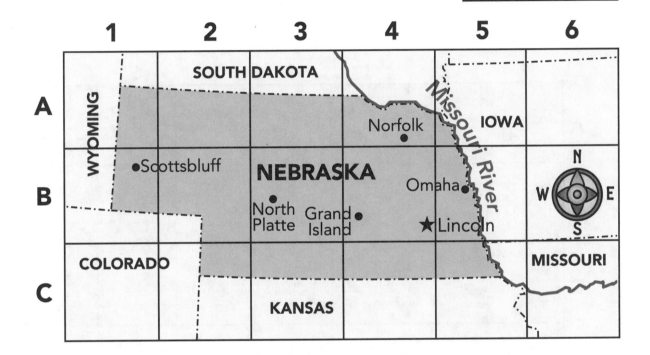

Use the map to answer the questions.

1. In what square is North Platte? _____

2. What city is in A4? _____

3. In what square is Nebraska's capital? _____

4. Name the squares that the Missouri River runs through. _____

5. What state takes up most of A1? _____

A City Map

This map shows New Orleans.

It is the biggest city in Louisiana.

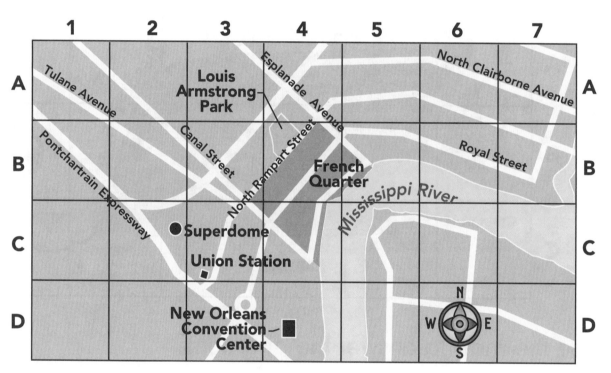

Use the map to answer the questions.

1. What river flows through New Orleans? _____

2. Why do you think people built a city on a river? _____

   _____

3. Sports teams play in the Superdome.
   In what square is this building? _____

Many people visit New Orleans each year.
The city is known for its jazz, a kind of music.

Louis Armstrong

4. Louis Armstrong was a famous trumpet player. What place is named for him in New Orleans? _____

5. Find C3. What building is there? _____

6. The French Quarter is the oldest part of New Orleans. In what squares is this part of the city? _____

7. Is the river east or west of the French Quarter? _____

Small Places...

Look at the maps on these pages.

Map 1 shows a city.
Map 2 shows a state.
Map 3 shows a country.
Are the places that these maps show all the same size?

A city is smaller than a state. A state is just one part of the United States. The maps are the same size on paper, but they show places of different sizes.

AUSTIN, TEXAS

Map 1

Use the maps to answer the questions.

1. **What city is shown on all three maps?** _____

2. **In what state is this city?** _____

3. **In what country is this city?** _____

4. **Is Texas larger or smaller than Austin?** _____

Large Places

TEXAS

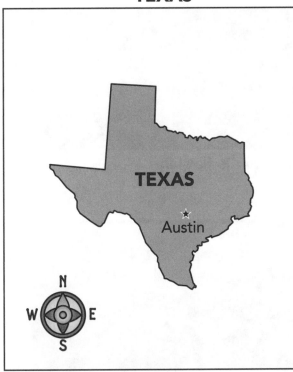

Map 2

UNITED STATES

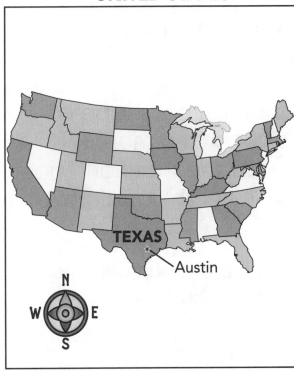

Map 3

5. Is Austin larger or smaller than the United States? _____

6. Is the United States larger or smaller than Texas? _____

7. Is Texas in the north or south
   part of the United States? _____

8. Which map would you use to
   find your way to the LBJ Library? _____

Landforms

These pictures show different parts of Earth called **landforms**.

A landform is a shape of land such as a mountain. You can see that Earth has many different landforms.

A **plain** is flat land.

A **valley** is low land between hills or mountains.

1. **How is a mountain different from a plain?**

   _____

2. **Through what kind of landform does a river often flow?**

   _____

3. **What are two ways you could get to an island?**

   _____

4. **Which type of land is best for farming?**

   Why? _____

A **mountain** is very high land.

A **hill** is land that is higher than a plain, but not as high as a mountain.

An **island** is land with water all around it.

5. Which landform is good for skiing? _____

   Why? _____

6. Which landforms can you see near your house?

   _____

   _____

Bodies of Water

Earth has different bodies of water, too.

An **ocean** is a large body of salt water.

A **river** is a long body of water that flows across the land.

A **lake** is water with land all around it.

Use the pictures to answer the questions.

1. Which body of water would take the longest time to cross? _____

2. What are some things you might do on a lake? _____

3. How are rivers and lakes different? _____

_____

The picture shows different kinds of land and water.

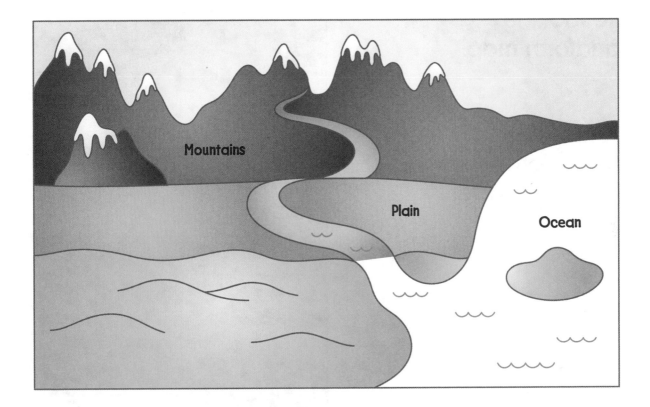

1. Find the low land between the mountains.
   Write valley on it.

2. Find the ocean. Color it blue.

3. Find land that has water all around it.
   Write the name on this land.

4. Find land that is higher than the plain, but not as high as the mountains. Add the correct label to this land.

Using a Landform Map

You are looking at a landform map.

This map shows where landforms and bodies of water are in Virginia.

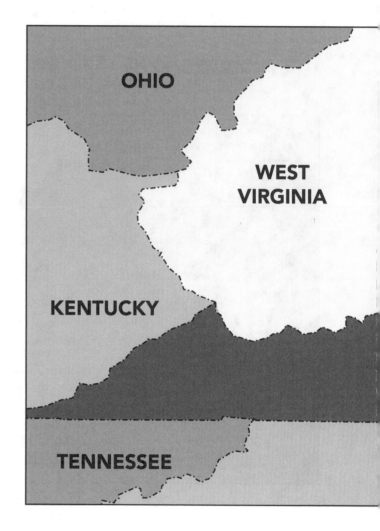

Use the map to answer the questions.

1. What does the symbol [   ] mean? _____

2. What is the symbol for plains? _____

3. Find the James River.
   Name the landforms it flows across. _____

4. Are mountains in the east or
   the west part of Virginia? _____

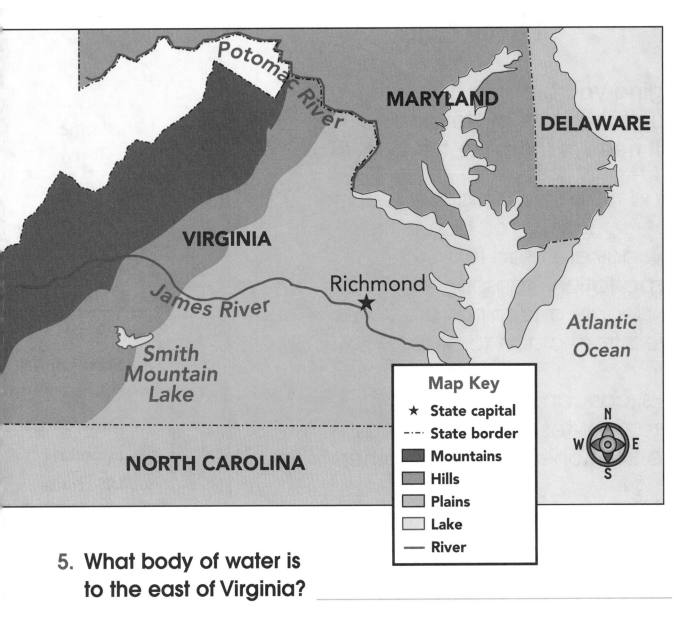

Map Key

★ State capital
-·-· State border
■ Mountains
■ Hills
■ Plains
□ Lake
— River

5. What body of water is to the east of Virginia? _____

6. What kind of land is near the capital of Virginia? _____

7. What river forms part of the border between Virginia and Maryland? _____

8. In which part of Virginia do you think there are more farms? _____ Why?

A Road Map

Imagine you are going on a drive through the state of Nevada. You'll need a map like this one.

A road map shows highways and other roads that you can travel on. Roads are used for transportation. Transportation is how people and things are moved from place to place.

Trucks, cars, and buses follow different routes. A route is a way to go from one place to another.

Use the map to answer the questions.

Pacific Ocean

Key

★ **State capital**

● **City**

‑‑‑ **State border**

(80) **Interstate**

(50) **U.S. route**

1. **Find Las Vegas. What highway would you take to get to Ely?** _____

   In which direction would you travel? _____

2. **A truck leaves Reno for Elko. On which highway does it drive?** _____

3. **From Tonopah, follow Highway 95 south. What city do you reach?** _____

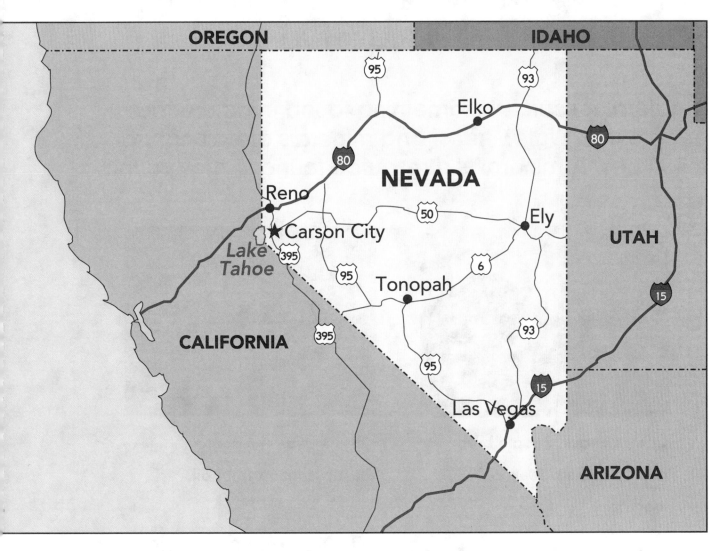

4. If you follow Highway 15 north and east
   from Las Vegas, what states do you reach? _____

5. What highway takes you from Elko to Utah? _____

   In which direction do you travel? _____

6. What highway links Carson City with California? _____

7. What are two routes you could
   take to go from Reno to Ely? _____

_____

A Resource Map

A **natural resource** is something found in nature that people use. Water, trees, and minerals are all natural resources. A mineral is a resource found in the ground.

Coal is a rock. People burn coal to make power for electricity.

Oil is a natural resource.

Plastic is made from oil.

Sand is made of rocks and minerals. Sand is used to make concrete for houses and sidewalks.

1. **Name two ways that you use water.**

   _____

   _____

2. **Name something that is made from plastic.**

   _____

3. **What natural resource is used to make a wooden chair?** _____

Many of Wyoming's resources are minerals. This resource map shows where some of Wyoming's minerals are found.

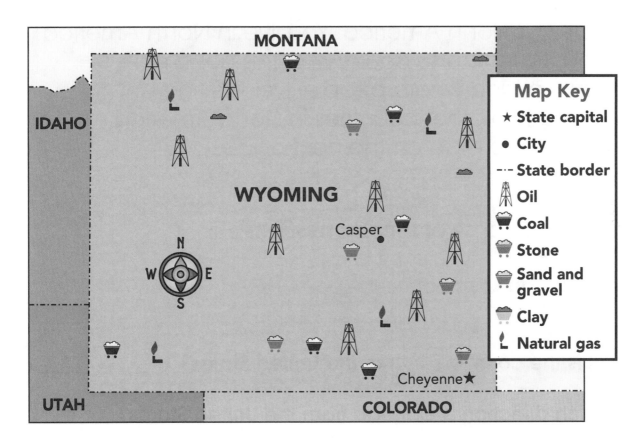

Circle YES or NO. Use the map to help you.

1. **Stone is found near Cheyenne.**   YES   NO

2. **Clay is mostly in the north part of Wyoming.**   YES   NO

3. **There is no coal in the west part of the state.** YES   NO

4. **Most of Wyoming's oil is in the west.**   YES   NO

5. **Wyoming has more coal than gravel.**   YES   NO

North America

Can you name Earth's seven continents?

One of them is North America. You live in North America.
The United States is one country on this continent.
A country is a land where people live. Mexico and
Canada are two other countries in North America.
Find them on the map on the next page.

Use the map to answer these questions.

1. **What does the symbol ———
   stand for?** _____

2. **What is the country south of the United States?** _____

3. **In which direction is Canada from the United States?** _____

4. **What is the capital of Mexico?** _____

5. **Is the Pacific Ocean to the east or
   west of North America?** _____

6. **What state is separated from the
   United States by Canada?** _____

7. **What river forms the border between
   the United States and Mexico?** _____

8. **Which country is larger, Canada or Mexico?** _____

Bering
Sea

ARCTIC
OCEAN

Bering Strait

Greenland
Sea

Alaska
(U.S.)

Beaufort
Sea

Greenland
(Denmark)

Gulf of
Alaska

Baffin
Bay

Nuuk

Not at same scale

Labrador
Sea

Hudson
Bay

Hawaii
(U.S.)

Canada

ROCKY MOUNTAINS

Mississippi
River

Ottawa ✪

ATLANTIC
OCEAN

Washington, D.C. ✪

**United States
of America**

PACIFIC
OCEAN

Rio
Grande

Bermuda (U.K.)

Bahamas

Mexico

Gulf of
Mexico

Cuba

Dominican
Republic

Mexico City ✪

Haiti

Puerto
Rico (U.S.)

Jamaica

Belize

North America

✪ National capital

Λ Mountains

— Border

Honduras

Nicaragua

Caribbean Sea

Guatemala

El Salvador

Costa Rica

Panama

SOUTH AMERICA

Area of detail

© Scholastic Inc.

Map Review 1

Use the map to answer the questions.

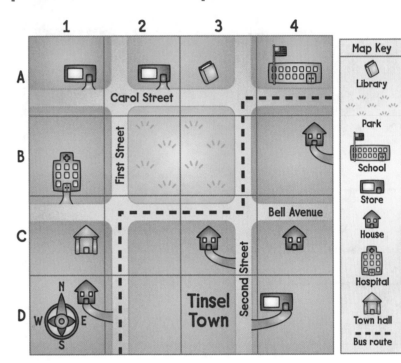

1. What does the symbol mean?

_____

2. What is the symbol for library?

_____

3. What does the letter "S" mean on the compass rose? _____

4. What is in square C1? _____

5. In which direction is the hospital from the park? _____

6. Is the school east or west of the library? _____

7. Amy lives on First Street. In what square is her house? _____

8. Amy takes the bus to school. Name the streets that the bus route follows.

_____

Map Review 2

Use the map to answer the questions.

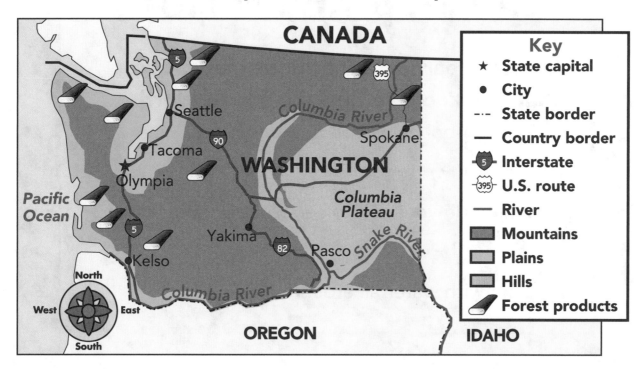

1. What does this symbol ——— mean? _____

2. What country is to the north of Washington? _____

3. What state is east of Washington? _____

4. What river forms the border
   between Washington and Oregon? _____

5. What is the capital of Washington? _____

6. What resource does Washington have? _____

7. What highway can you take from Kelso to Seattle? _____

Thinking About Maps

You have learned a lot about maps. Use what you know to find the secret words.

1. This symbol helps you find directions.

   ___ ___ ___ ___ ___ ___ ___ ___ ___
         1   4

2. Where do you look to see what symbols mean?

   ___ ___ ___ ___ ___ ___
      3

3. Land with water all around it.

   ___ ___ ___ ___ ___ ___
       2

4. Plains and hills are types of

   ___ ___ ___ ___ ___ ___ ___
    5   8   6

5. North America is a

   ___ ___ ___ ___ ___ ___ ___
    10   7

6. This landform is very high land.

   ___ ___ ___ ___ ___ ___ ___
    9

Now, can you figure out the secret message?

___ ___ ___ ___   ___ ___ ___   ___ ___ ___
1 2 3 4   5 6 7   8 9 10

Glossary

border
A border shows where places begin and end.

capital
A capital is a city where government leaders work. Washington, D.C., is the capital of the United States.

compass rose
A compass rose is a symbol that helps you read a map. A compass rose shows the four main directions.

continent
A continent is a large body of land. Earth has seven continents.

country
A country is a land where people live. The United States is a country.

direction
A direction tells where something is. The four main directions are north, south, east, and west.

distance
Distance is how far it is from one place to another.

globe
A globe is a model of Earth.

grid
A grid is a pattern of lines that form squares.

hill
A hill is land that is higher than a plain but not as high as a mountain.

island
An island is land with water all around it.

lake
A lake is a body of water with land all around it.

landform
A landform is a shape of land such as a mountain.

Glossary

map
A map is a drawing of a place from above. A map shows where things are.

map key
A map key is a list of symbols on a map. A map key tells what each symbol means.

mountain
A mountain is very high land.

natural resource
A natural resource is something found in nature that people use. Coal is a natural resource.

ocean
An ocean is a large body of salt water. Earth has five oceans.

plain
A plain is flat land.

river
A river is a long body of water that flows across the land.

road map
A road map shows highways and other roads that people can travel on.

route
A route is a way to go from one place to another.

symbol
A symbol is a drawing that stands for something real. A symbol can also be a color or a pattern.

transportation
Transportation is how people and things are moved from place to place. Highways are used for transportation.

valley
A valley is low land between hills or mountains.

© Scholastic Inc.

SCIENCE

Friends of Long Ago

A **paleontologist** is a person who studies dinosaurs. Several dinosaurs that paleontologists have studied are listed below. Use the letters in *paleontologist* to write the names of these dinosaurs below their meanings.

1. "Winged and Toothless" p _ _ _ a _ _ _ _	2. "Double Beamed" l _ _ _ _ _ _ _ _
3. "Great Lizard" _ e _ _ _ o _ _ _ _ _	4. "Iguana Tooth" _ _ _ _ n _ _ _ _
5. "Deceptive Lizard" _ _ _ t o _ _ _ _ _	6. "Speedy Thief" _ _ l o _ _ _ _ _ _
7. "Roofed Lizard" _ _ g _ _ _ _ _ _	8. "Arm Lizard" _ _ _ _ _ i _ _ _ _ _ _
9. "Different Lizard" _ _ _ _ s _ _ _ _	10. "Three-Horned Face" t _ _ _ _ _ _ _ _ _

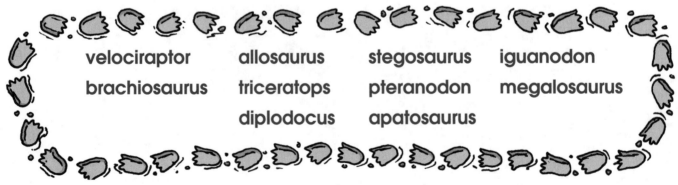

velociraptor   allosaurus   stegosaurus   iguanodon

brachiosaurus   triceratops   pteranodon   megalosaurus

diplodocus   apatosaurus

 Research one of the dinosaurs above. On another sheet of paper, write five words that describe this dinosaur.

Tricks of the Light

Read about how animals use light and shadow to stay alive. Then try the science investigations.

Black Heron

This bird wades in water, looking for tasty fish. There's just one problem. The water's surface acts like a mirror. Sunlight reflects off the surface and into the bird's eyes. The bird can't see past the reflections to the fish below.

But this bird has a trick. It spreads its wings into an umbrella shape. That blocks the light. It makes a dark shadow on the water's surface. The shadow helps it look into the water. When a fish swims into its shadow, the heron can see it and . . . **GULP!**

Atolla Jellyfish

This jellyfish lives deep in the ocean—so deep that no sunlight reaches it. Creatures there live mostly in the dark. But when they need it, many can make their own light.

This atolla jellyfish uses light for protection. If a predator tries to eat it, the jellyfish flashes a ring of blue lights. The lights act like a burglar alarm. Instead of a police officer, the lights attract a large squid. The squid rushes to the rescue and eats the predator. The jellyfish is saved!

Investigation 1

Play with light and shadows to make a fun puppet show!

1. Gather the materials you will need.

2. Make a shadow puppet: Draw a person, monster, or animal on the cardboard. Draw a handle from the bottom of the puppet to the bottom of the cardboard. Cut out your puppet.

3. Turn off the lights in the room. Turn on the flashlight. Hold the puppet between the flashlight and a blank wall. Does it make a shadow on the wall?

4. Experiment with your puppet and your flashlight. By moving them around, how can you do each of these "special effects"?

   • Make the puppet's shadow grow bigger.

   • Make the puppet's shadow shrink.

   • Make the puppet's shadow a thin sliver.

   • Make the puppet's shadow move without moving the puppet.

5. Use your shadow puppet and special effects to perform a short show.

Materials

★ cardboard

★ pencil

★ scissors

★ flashlight

★ recording sheet (next page)

© Scholastic Inc.

Experiment with your puppet and your flashlight by moving them around. Record your observations below.

How did you make the puppet's shadow grow bigger?	**How did you make the puppet's shadow shrink?**
How did you make the puppet's shadow a thin sliver?	**How did you make the puppet's shadow move without moving the puppet?**

Investigation 2

What material blocks light the best?
What lets light through? Try this!

1. Gather the materials you will need.

2. Fold an index card in half and cut out a simple shape. Unfold. Do the same with the two other index cards.

3. Hold one card over a blank sheet of paper. Shine a flashlight through the hole in the card. What do you see on the paper? How much light comes through the hole?

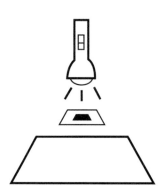

4. Cut a piece of waxed paper a little bigger than the hole. Tape it over the hole in one card.

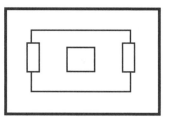

5. Repeat Step 3 with aluminum foil and plastic wrap.

6. Look at your cards. How much light do you think could go through each material? Write your prediction on the next page.

7. Repeat Step 2 with each of your materials. Record your observations on your recording sheet.

8. Imagine your materials were thicker. Which would make the best window? Which would make the best curtain? Which would make the best wall?

Materials
★ 3 index cards
★ scissors
★ blank paper
★ flashlight
★ waxed paper
★ tape
★ aluminum foil
★ plastic wrap
★ recording sheet (next page)

1. Do Steps 2 and 3 of the investigation. What do you see on the paper? How much light comes through the hole?

   Check one: ☐ a lot   ☐ some   ☐ none

2. Now do Steps 4–7 of the investigation. Record your predictions and observations in the chart below.

Material	I predict the material will let through this much light	I observed the material let through this much light
Waxed paper	☐ a lot ☐ some ☐ none	☐ a lot ☐ some ☐ none
Aluminum foil	☐ a lot ☐ some ☐ none	☐ a lot ☐ some ☐ none
Plastic	☐ a lot ☐ some ☐ none	☐ a lot ☐ some ☐ none

3. Imagine your materials were thicker. Which would make the best window? The best curtain? The best wall?

_____

_____

_____

_____

Hamster or Gerbil?

Read the science article.
Then follow the directions in the Text Marking box.

Hamster

Gerbil

At first glance, hamsters and gerbils look alike. Both are soft and adorable rodents. Both make good pets. Can you tell them apart?

One way is to compare how they look. They can be the same size, but look at their tails. A hamster tail is short and stubby. A gerbil tail is as long as the rest of its body. Now notice their heads. The hamster's head is round with chubby cheeks. The gerbil's head is narrow, like a mouse's.

Or you could compare habits. A gerbil plays all day and sleeps at night. In contrast, a hamster sleeps during the day. Suppose you have one of each. If the sound of little feet running on a wheel wakes you up at night, you can probably blame your hamster.

Text Marking

Compare and contrast hamsters and gerbils.

☐ Draw boxes around the signal words **both**, **but**, and **in contrast**.

◯ Circle one way they are alike.

___ Underline one way they are different.

Answer each question. Give details from the article.

1. Your "first glance" is when you _____ something for the first time.

○ A. hear   ○ B. think   ○ C. touch   ○ D. look at

What helped you answer? _____

_____

_____

2. Which is NOT true about gerbils?

○ A. Gerbils are rodents.   ○ C. Gerbils have long tails.

○ B. Gerbils play at night.   ○ D. Gerbils have narrow heads.

What helped you answer? _____

_____

_____

3. Describe two ways that hamsters and gerbils look different.

_____

_____

4. Explain one way that hamsters and gerbils act differently.

_____

_____

© Scholastic Inc.

No Teeth? No Problem!

Read the nature article.
Then follow the directions in the Text Marking box.

The giant anteater has a perfect name. It's very big, and it eats ants— thousands of them a day. And it doesn't even have teeth!

This animal's head fits its needs. It has a **keen** sense of smell. It sniffs out an anthill with its powerful nose. Then it uses its sharp claws to open a hole in the anthill. Now its long, wormlike tongue gets busy. The anteater pokes its tongue deep into the hole. Ants stick to it. The anteater snaps its tongue back into its mouth. It scrapes the ants off and swallows them whole.

But feeding like this isn't easy. Ants sting the tongue. So the anteater must stop to rest it after a minute or so. It goes back later for more, after its tongue stops hurting.

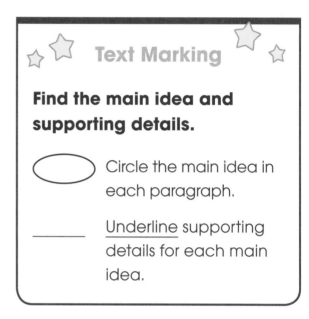

Text Marking

Find the main idea and supporting details.

⬭   Circle the main idea in each paragraph.

___   Underline supporting details for each main idea.

A giant anteater

Its long tongue

Answer each question. Give details from the article.

1. Which is the most important topic of the article?

   ○ A. living without teeth   ○ C. kinds of tongues

   ○ B. insects that sting   ○ D. giant anteaters

   What helped you answer? _____

   _____

   _____

2. The author says that the giant anteater has a **keen** sense of smell. Which word means about the same as **keen**?

   ○ A. weak   ○ B. strong   ○ C. unusual   ○ D. surprising

   What helped you answer? _____

   _____

   _____

3. Why does the author say that the giant anteater has a perfect name?

   _____

   _____

4. Look at the pictures. How do its body parts help it get food?

   _____

   _____

Reptile and Amphibian Fun

Unscramble these reptile and amphibian words.

leturt _____   toraglila _____

skena _____   zildar _____

grof _____   colideroc _____

adot _____   trtooise _____

Answer these questions. Use the words in the Word Bank.

1. Frogs start life as _____ .

2. Frogs and toads are _____ .

3. Snakes have no _____ .

4. All reptiles are _____ -blooded.

5. Some tortoises can live to be _____ years old.

6. Turtles, crocodiles, lizards, and snakes are _____ .

WORD BANK
100
amphibians
cold
legs
reptiles
tadpoles

© Scholastic Inc.

Interesting Insect Facts

Use the labels on the diagram to complete the sentences below.

head
thorax
legs
stinger

antennae
eyes
wings
abdomen

An insect's __ __ __ __ includes the __ __ __ __ and
      3   9

__ __ __ __ __ __ __ __ . Three pairs of __ __ __ __ are connected to
10   2   6

the __ __ __ __ __ __ . Most insects have one or two pair of __ __ __ __ __ __ .
    8 1

The tip of the __ __ __ __ __ __ __ may have a tube for laying eggs
          7   4

or a __ __ __ __ __ __ __ .
      5

Use the number code above to learn some interesting facts about insects.

There are more than __ __ __ __ __ __ __ __ __ kinds of insects.
                 1 2 3   4 5 6 6 5 1 2

The Goliath __ __ __ __ __ __ grows to more than four inches long.
          7 3 3 8 6 3

An __ __ __ __ __ moth is about 1,000 times larger than a tiny fairy fly.
   10 8 6 10 9

Insect Word Search

Find the words from the Word Bank in the puzzle below.

WORD BANK

ANT	BEE	BEETLE	BUTTERFLY	GRASSHOPPER
MOTH	ROACH	CRICKET	LADYBUG	MOSQUITO

```
G  R  A  S  S  H  O  P  P  E  R  C
B  W  E  R  L  A  D  Y  B  U  G  R
E  Y  B  U  T  T  E  R  F  L  Y  I
E  U  I  K  M  N  A  N  T  F  F  C
M  O  T  H  L  J  K  U  Y  S  A  K
R  T  E  Q  A  R  O  A  C  H  O  E
B  E  E  T  L  E  Y  S  I  M  P  T
N  F  H  J  M  O  S  Q  U  I  T  O
```

The Biggest Cave in the World

Read about a cave in Vietnam. Then try the science investigations.

Water seeps through cracks in the rocky ground. The water slowly **dissolves**, or melts away, some of the rock. Then the water carries the dissolved rock away. This process is called **erosion**. Over thousands of years, the water carves out a larger and larger space. A cave is formed!

This process can also make new shapes inside a cave. Some look like rock icicles hanging down from the ceiling. These are called stalactites. Some look like rock piles that grow from the ground. These are called **stalagmites**.

These rock shapes can make caves look like works of art. But Earth's caves will never be finished. Water will keep shaping them . . . very, very slowly.

Investigation 1

Some rocks dissolve more quickly than others.
Find out how that helps form caves.

Materials

★ clay (about the size of a large marble)

★ sugar cube

★ eyedropper or pipette

★ bowl

★ cup of water

★ recording sheet (next page)

1. Gather the materials you need.

2. Squish the clay flat into a strip. Wrap the strip around the sugar cube, as shown below. Make sure there are two openings in the clay—one at the top and one at the bottom.

3. Put the clay and sugar cube against the inside of a bowl, as shown below. The clay and sugar are like two different rocks. Some rocks dissolve more easily than others.

4. Predict: What do you think will happen if you drip 100 drops of water onto your rocks? Write your prediction on the next page.

5. Use your dropper to pick up water. Drip it onto your model rocks. Count the drops. After every 20 drops, stop and record what you notice on your recording sheet.

6. How is your model like a cave? How is it different?

clay

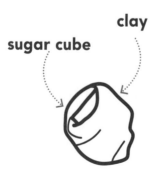

sugar cube · clay

© Scholastic Inc.

1. Do Steps 2–4 of the investigation. **Predict**: What do you think will happen if you drip 100 drops of water onto your "rocks"?

_____

2. Now do Step 5 of the investigation. Record what you notice.

What I noticed about my rocks	
after 20 drops	
after 40 drops	
after 60 drops	
after 80 drops	
after 100 drops	

3. How is your model like a cave? How is it different?

_____

_____

Investigation 2

Erosion helps form caves. But it can also wash away soil. How can erosion be stopped?

1. Gather the materials you will need.

2. Put the same amount of soil into two milk carton halves. For each one, fill the closed end a little more than halfway full. Let the soil slope down to the open end. Gently pat the soil smooth.

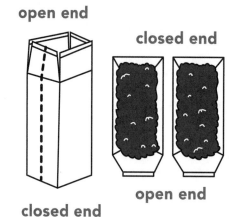

open end

closed end

closed end

open end

Materials

★ quart-size milk carton, fully opened on top and cut in half lengthwise

★ soil

★ trowel or large spoon

★ watering can with sprinkler head

★ water

★ measuring cup

★ building block

★ inventor's materials: toothpicks, pipe cleaners, index cards, paper towels, plastic forks

★ recording sheet (next page)

3. Set one carton on the ground outdoors. Prop up the closed end on a building block.

4. Put 2 cups of water into a watering can. Pour the water over the soil at the closed end of your carton. Let it drain out completely. What do you notice? Do you see signs of erosion? Record what you see on the next page.

5. Think: How can you keep water from eroding the soil? (**Hint:** Plant roots spread through soil and help keep it in place.)
Write three ideas on your recording sheet.

6. Choose one of your ideas from Step 5. Gather your inventor's materials and your second milk carton half. Add your invention to stop erosion to the soil.

7. Do Steps 3 and 4 again with your second carton.

8. Compare the two cartons. How well did your invention stop erosion? How could you improve your invention?

1. Do Steps 2–4 of the investigation. Record what you see.

_____

_____

2. How can you keep the water from eroding the soil? Write three ideas.

_____

_____

3. Now do Steps 6 and 7 of the investigation. What do you notice?

_____

_____

4. Compare the two cartons. How well did your invention stop erosion?

_____

_____

5. How could you improve your invention?

_____

_____

Changes in Rocks

How are *erosion* and *weathering* related?

Most rocks are so hard you may think they can't break. But many forces break down rocks. It doesn't take a hammer or machine. Nature itself can change rocks.

Erosion is the word scientists use for when things wear away. When big rocks **erode**, little bits of them break off. Erosion makes rocks change their size and shape. Weather causes some kinds of erosion. This kind of erosion is called **weathering**. Changes from weathering take a long time.

Weathering by Water When it rains, water gets into cracks in rocks. If the weather gets very cold, the water can freeze. Frozen water takes up more space than liquid water. So ice in a rock can make it crack or break.

Weathering by Wind Blowing winds can carry dust and pebbles that hit against big rocks. Bit by bit, all that rubbing erodes the rock. So weathering by wind causes changes in size and shape.

Weathering by Waves Ocean waves are strong. They move toward the land and crash into rocks at the shore. As waves hit the rocks again and again, little bits chip off. In time, many of those little chips turn into sand.

Answer each question. Give evidence from the article.

1. What does *erosion* do to big rocks?

  ○ A. It gets them wet.   ○ C. It breaks them down.

  ○ B. It builds them up.   ○ D. It makes them heavier.

What helped you pick your answer? _____

_____

2. Which sentence about weathering is TRUE?

  ○ A. Weathering happens very quickly.

  ○ B. Weathering must take place near water.

  ○ C. Weathering works only on broken rock.

  ○ D. Weathering takes place over a long time.

How did you pick your answer? _____

_____

3. Explain how wind erodes big rocks. _____

_____

_____

4. Describe the kind of weathering that changed the rock in each picture.

_____

_____

_____

Earthquake!

Read the article about an earthquake that happened during the 1989 World Series. Then follow the directions in the Text Marking box.

Thousands of fans fill Candlestick Park in San Francisco. A handful of ballplayers are on the field. They are stretching, chatting, and warming up. The start of Game 3 of the 1989 World Series between the Giants and the Oakland Athletics is moments away. Excitement fills the air.

Players and fans evacuate the stadium during the 1989 World Series

Suddenly, everything changes. The huge stadium begins to rumble and swing. Lights go out. Cracks form and chunks of concrete fall from the upper deck. **Alarmed** fans head for the exits. What happened?

What happened is that rock beneath the Earth's surface had suddenly moved. Then the ground began to shake. San Francisco was having a major earthquake!

Bridges buckled and buildings swayed. Highways collapsed. The earthquake caused a halt in the World Series. The games didn't start up again for ten days.

Text Marking

Find the cause and effects of the earthquake.

☐ Draw boxes around the signal words.

◯ Circle the cause.

___ Underline the effects.

Answer each question. Give details from the article.

1. The word **alarmed** probably means _____.

   ○ A. excited   ○ B. loud   ○ C. afraid   ○ D. quiet

What helped you answer? _____

_____

_____

2. Which was NOT an effect of the earthquake?

   ○ A. People lost interest in baseball.   ○ D. Game 3 was delayed.

   ○ B. The stadium had to be repaired.   ○ C. Bridges had to be fixed.

What helped you answer? _____

_____

_____

3. Why did fans at the stadium want to leave?

_____

_____

4. What makes earthquakes so dangerous?

_____

_____

A Flower's Job

Use the words in the box to label each part of the flower and to complete the sentences below.

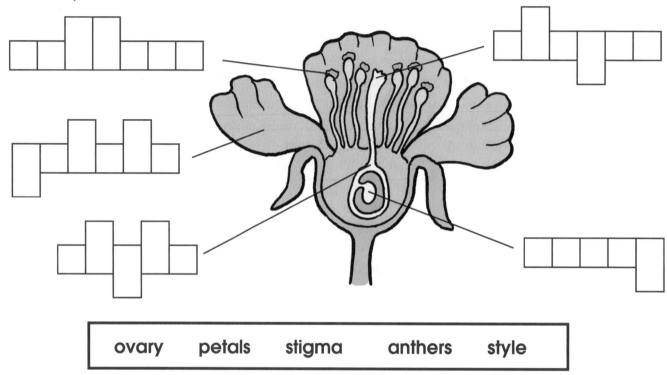

| ovary | petals | stigma | anthers | style |

A flower is important in the life cycle of a plant because it contains the parts for reproduction. The colorful _ _ t _ _ _ and sepals protect the flower when it is in bud. The sticky part in the middle of the flower is the _ _ _ g _ _ . Around the stigma are a _ _ _ _ _ _ which are tiny stems with knobs on top. Inside the anthers is a golden dust called pollen. In the base of the flower is the _ v _ _ _ . Growing out of the ovary is the _ _ y _ _ . When ripe, the anthers burst open sending out clouds of pollen. The pollen is carried to the stigma of another flower. This is called pollination.

Is This a Plant?

**Read about these amazing plants.
Then try the science investigations.**

The **giant sequoia** (seh-KOY-uh) tree is one of the tallest plants on Earth. Water travels from its roots all the way to the top. It takes almost a month!

Most plants grow from seeds. In many plants, like the **sunflower**, seeds develop inside flowers. Animals, like birds, eat the seeds. They help spread seeds to new places to grow.

Watch out, bugs! The **Venus flytrap** has a taste for insects. Most plants get food from soil. But this one traps bugs instead.

The **cactus** has a thick, waxy stem and leaves. These store water. Its prickly spines keep away thirsty animals.

giant sequoia

sunflower

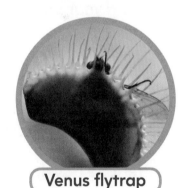

Venus flytrap

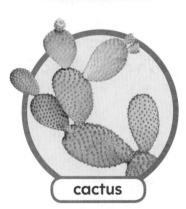

cactus

Investigation 1

In the hot, dry desert, plant leaves need to hold on to water. What kind of leaf stays wet in the desert? Find out here.

Materials

★ 3 moist paper towels

★ cookie sheet

★ wax paper

★ 2 paper clips

★ recording sheet (next page)

1. Gather the materials you will need.

2. Spread out one wet paper towel on the cookie sheet. This is Leaf 1.

3. Roll up the other two paper towels. Put one on the cookie sheet. This is Leaf 2.

4. Wrap the third paper towel in wax paper. Use a paper clip to keep each end closed. This is Leaf 3.

5. Put the cookie sheet in a warm, dry place. **Predict:** How will the leaves change after one day? Record your prediction on the next page.

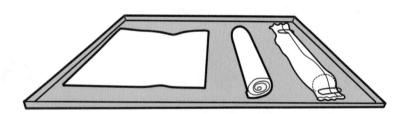

6. After one day, feel your leaves. How have they changed? Record on the next page.

7. Which leaf keeps water in best? Which would make a good desert leaf? Which would not?

1. Do Steps 2–5 of the investigation. **Predict:** How will the leaves change after one day? Record your prediction in the chart below.

2. After one day, feel your leaves. How have they changed? Record below.

	My Prediction	**What Happened**
Leaf 1		
Leaf 2		
Leaf 3		

3. Which leaf keeps water in best? Which would make a good desert leaf? Which would not? Write your answers on a separate sheet of paper.

Investigation 2

How do seeds get to good growing places? Try this!

1. Gather the materials you will need.

2. **Think:** What's the first thing seeds need? A good growing place! But how do they get there? Read "How Seeds Go" for some clues.

3. Look at your seed (popcorn kernel). How would you like it to travel? Will it glide through the air? Float on the water? Or will it stick to an animal passing by?

4. Test your seed. Can it travel the way you want? (Can it glide, float, or stick?) If not, change your seed. Add something to it. What things will you use?

5. Test your seed again. Did your seed pass its test? If not, make more changes.

6. When your seed passes the test, draw it on the next page. Tell how you changed your seed.

7. **Think:** Can your seed travel another way? How can you change it so it can?

Materials

★ popcorn kernel

★ things to make your seed go (for example, tape, cotton, tissue paper, string, velcro)

★ recording sheet (next page)

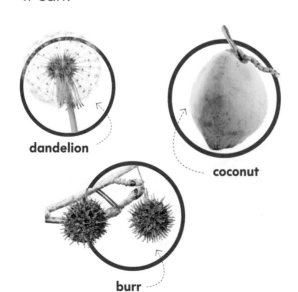

dandelion

coconut

burr

How Seeds Go

Some seeds glide.

Fluffy dandelion seeds are blown around by the wind. Will your seed glide through the air? Put it on your hand and blow. How far does it go?

Some seeds float.

Coconuts can float away in water. Will your seed float in water? Put it in a dishpan of water. Does it float or sink?

Some seeds stick.

Burrs are covered with little hooks that can hitch a ride on animals. Will your seed stick to an animal passing by? Press the seed onto a stuffed animal. How long does it stick?

1. Do Steps 2 and 3 of the investigation. How would your seed travel?

_____

2. Now do Step 4 of the investigation. How will you change your seed?

_____

3. Do Step 5 of the investigation. Tell what other changes you made.

_____

4. When your seed passes its test, draw it in the box below.
Tell how you changed your seed.

5. Think: Can your seed travel another way? How can you change
it so it can? Record your ideas on a separate sheet of paper.

Wonderful Weather

Add or subtract from each letter to spell different weather words.
The first one has been done for you.

| - | a | b | c | d | e | f | g | h | i | j | k | l | m | n | o | p | q | r | s | t | u | v | w | x | y | z | + |

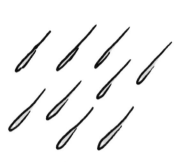

r a i n
o + 3   b − 1   g + 2   (r − 4)

○
e − 2   j + 2   p − 1   (w − 2)   c + 1   v + 3

○
d + 2   q + 1   r − 3   r + 1   (s + 1)

○
v − 2   (l + 3)   v − 4   l + 2   c − 2   g − 3   n + 1

○
d − 2   i + 3   h + 1   x + 2   v + 4   a + 0   p + 2   (g − 3)

○
k + 1   f + 3   h − 1   (k − 3)   r + 2   o − 1   f + 3   l + 2   j − 3

○
q + 2   t + 1   p − 2   r + 1   f + 2   k − 2   k + 3   (a + 4)

Unscramble the circled letters to
spell weather you hear but cannot see ___ ___ ___ ___ ___ ___

What's the Weather?

Read about the weather. Then try the science investigations.

A lot of what we do depends on the weather. We have to know how to get dressed for school, work, or even a picnic! If bad weather is coming, we want to know about it. We need to get ready!

How can we tell what the weather will be? One tool is a **thermometer**. It shows how hot or cold the air is. Another tool is a **wind sock**. It shows which way the wind blows.

The sky can also tell us the weather! Different **clouds** bring different kinds of weather.

Common Clouds

Cumulus (KYOOM-yoo-lus)
If you see clouds like this, the weather will be nice.

Cirrus (SIR-us)
If you see clouds like this, the weather is nice but may be changing.

Stratus (STRAY-tus)
If you see clouds like this, it might rain a little.

Cumulonimbus (KYOOM-yoo-loh-NIM-bus)
If you see clouds like this, it might rain a lot!

Investigation 1

**Scientists look for patterns in the weather.
These patterns help them predict future weather.**

1. Write today's date in the first column on your Cloud Tracker chart.

2. Look at the sky in the morning. Can you see any clouds?

   • **No:** Write "no clouds" on your chart.

   • **Yes:** Compare the clouds to the pictures below your Cloud Tracker chart. If they match one of the clouds, write down what kind. If not, describe the clouds or write "unknown."

3. Notice what the weather is like in late afternoon. Is there rain or snow falling? If so, is there a lot or just a little? Is it windy? Record the weather on your chart.

4. Check the weather again at bedtime. Record it on your chart.

5. Do Steps 1–4 on four different days. (Try to check the clouds at the same time each day.)

6. Look at your Cloud Tracker chart. Do you see any patterns?

Cloud Tracker

Date				
Kinds of clouds in the morning				
Weather in late afternoon				
Weather at bedtime				

Common Clouds

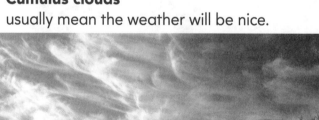

Cumulus clouds
usually mean the weather will be nice.

Stratus clouds
often bring drizzles of rain.

Cirrus clouds
can mean the weather may be changing.

Cumulonimbus clouds
usually bring heavy rain and lightning.

Look at your chart. Do you see any patterns in the weather?
Write your answer on a separate sheet of paper.

Investigation 2

Weather experts use tools to learn about the weather. Make your own weather tool!

1. Read about these three weather tools. Pick one you would like to make.

   - A **wind vane** shows which way the wind is blowing. The arrow points to where the wind is coming from.

   - An **anemometer** (an-i-MOM-uh-tur) measures wind speed. It uses three or four small cups. When the wind blows, it makes the cups spin.

   - A **rain gauge** (GAYJ) measures how much rain falls. A container collects the rainwater. Then a ruler can tell how many inches of rain fell.

2. **Think:** What weather tool would you like to make? Do you want to see which way the wind is blowing? Measure the wind speed? Measure the amount of rainfall? What would you need to make your weather tool? How would it work?

3. Draw your weather tool on the next page. Label your drawing. Write what you would use to make it and how it works. Then gather the materials you will need to make the tool.

<table>
<tr><td>

Materials

★ inventor's materials: cardboard, paper or plastic cups, metal can, plastic bottle, ruler, marker

★ recording sheet (next page)

</td></tr>
</table>

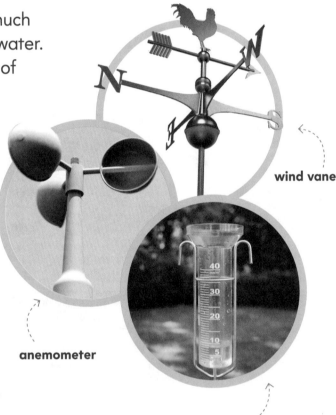

wind vane

anemometer

rain gauge

1. What weather tool would you like to make? (Check one.)

☐ Wind vane   ☐ Anemometer   ☐ Rain gauge

2. Draw your weather tool below. Label your drawing. Write what you would use to make it and how it works. Then use the materials you have gathered to make the tool.

Spring Weather Word Find

Find the words from the Word Bank in the puzzle below.

WORD BANK

CLOUDY	COOL	WINDY	FAIR	HOT	MILD
RAINY	SHOWERS	THUNDER	STORMY	SUNNY	TEMPERATURE

```
F  K  I  W  I  N  D  Y  A  C  S  O  O  S
A  I  S  G  S  M  R  O  L  G  U  N  S  H
I  S  T  O  R  M  Y  U  T  R  O  T  B  O
R  O  E  L  P  U  C  O  O  L  S  H  D  W
A  K  P  T  E  M  P  E  R  A  T  U  R  E
C  O  T  S  L  B  Y  H  O  T  R  N  M  R
L  E  L  I  N  M  S  B  R  T  U  D  J  S
O  C  V  B  F  X  U  H  E  S  T  E  A  D
U  L  B  F  B  T  N  Z  S  O  M  R  E  G
D  X  F  R  A  I  N  Y  R  Y  C  H  Z  H
Y  M  T  P  S  Q  Y  T  G  D  M  I  L  D
```

On a separate sheet of paper, write about springtime weather.
Use four words from the puzzle in your writing.

Music Makers and Shakers

**Read about vibrations in music.
Then try the science investigations.**

When something **vibrates**, it moves back and forth very quickly. Try this: Put your fingers on your throat and say, "vibrations." Can you feel your throat vibrate when you talk? Everything that makes a sound is vibrating, even if you can't see it moving.

How do musicians make their instruments vibrate? A drum is one of the simplest instruments. When you tap the skin of a drum, it vibrates. A harp is played by plucking metal strings. The strings are different lengths. Short strings vibrate quickly. They make high, squeaky sounds. Long strings vibrate slowly. They make low, deep sounds.

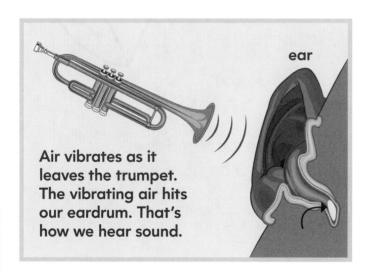

ear

Air vibrates as it leaves the trumpet. The vibrating air hits our eardrum. That's how we hear sound.

When an instrument vibrates, the air around it vibrates too. The vibrations travel through the air like waves in water. If the sound is loud enough to reach your ears, it vibrates your eardrums. Your ears send signals to your brain. You hear music!

Investigation 1

How can you see what sound looks like? Try this!

1. Gather the materials you will need.

2. Cut one side of a balloon from neck to bottom, as shown. Stretch the balloon tight over the top of a can. Have a partner use a rubber band to hold the balloon in place.

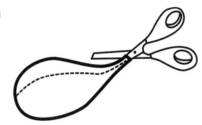

3. Sprinkle a little puffed rice cereal on top of the balloon.

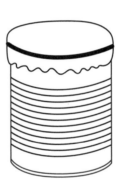

4. Roll the paper or file folder into a megaphone shape, as shown. Make sure there is an opening to speak into. Tape in place.

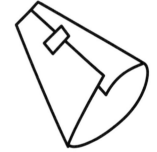

5. Point your megaphone at the balloon and shout. (Don't blow!) Record what happens on the next page.

6. Think: What made the cereal do what it did? How do you know? (Use the word *vibrate* in your answer.)

7. Try a shout that's high and squeaky. Then try one that's low and deep. Make loud sounds. Make soft sounds. Do different sounds make the cereal move differently? Record what you notice.

Materials
- ★ balloon
- ★ scissors
- ★ large empty tin can
- ★ rubber band
- ★ puffed rice cereal
- ★ stiff paper or file folder
- ★ tape
- ★ recording sheet (next page)

1. Do Steps 2–5 of the investigation. Record what happened.

_____

2. Think: What made the cereal do what it did? How do you know? (Use the word *vibrate* in your answer.)

_____

_____

3. Now do Step 7 of the investigation. Record what you notice below.

Type of sound	What happens to the cereal?
High and squeaky	
Low and deep	
Loud	
Soft	

Investigation 2

Play with sound, then make a musical instrument!

1. Gather the materials you will need.

2. Stretch a rubber band between your thumb and a finger. Pluck it. What do you observe?

3. Stretch the band around a cup, as shown. Pluck it. Does the cup change the sound's volume—how loud or quiet it is?

Materials
★ rubber band

★ plastic cup or other container

★ inventor's materials: cardboard boxes, more rubber bands, cardboard tubes, yogurt containers, tape, scissors, string

★ recording sheet (next page)

4. Pluck the rubber band again. Then touch the middle of the rubber band with one finger. This splits the rubber band in half. Pluck one of the halves. Compare the two sounds. Which has a higher sound—the longer (whole) rubber band or the shorter (half) rubber band? Can you play different notes by changing where you touch the rubber band?

5. Stretch the rubber band so it is tighter across the top of the cup. Does this change the sound? How?

6. Use what you have learned to make an instrument. Look at your inventor's materials. **Think:** How will you make your instrument loud enough to hear? How will you make different notes?

7. How does your instrument work? Explain on the next page.

1. Do Step 2 of the investigation.
What did you observe?

_____

_____

2. Now do Step 3 of the investigation. Is the sound
louder or quieter?

_____

3. Do Step 4 of the investigation. Which makes a higher sound—the longer
(whole) rubber band or the shorter (half) rubber band?

_____

4. Do Step 5 of the investigation. Does stretching the rubber band tight
across the cup change the sound? How?

_____

_____

5. Make an instrument. Explain how it works on a separate sheet of paper.

A Hidden Message

Why is it important to follow the directions?

It's fun and easy to make invisible paint. It uses normal materials most people already have. Gather up everything you need. Then follow the steps to surprise your friends.

What You Need

- tablespoon measure
- baking soda
- paper cup
- water
- mixing stick
- paintbrush
- plain white paper

What You Do

1. Measure 3 tablespoons of baking soda into the paper cup.

2. Add 4 tablespoons of water to the cup. Mix until all lumps are gone.

3. Dip a paintbrush into the "paint." Write a message on the paper.

4. Let the paint dry until your message disappears!

5. Hold the paper in front of a lit lightbulb.
   The heat will turn the baking soda brown.
   Your message will reappear!

Answer each question. Give evidence from the instructions.

1. Which word in the first paragraph means "cannot be seen"?

○ A. easy   ○ B. normal   ○ C. surprise   ○ D. invisible

What helped you pick your answer? _____

_____

2. What will surprise your friends?

○ A. An invisible message reappears.

○ B. Most of the materials are easy to find.

○ C. You can paint with baking soda.

○ D. Mixing makes lumps go away.

How did you pick your answer? _____

_____

_____

3. What do you do after you write a message on the paper?

_____

_____

4. Why are the **What You Do** steps numbered?

_____

_____

A Twitchy Muscle

Read the biology article.
Then follow the directions in the Text Marking box.

Most people know how the hiccups feel. Your body jumps inside. A "Hic!" sound pops out of your mouth. The hics repeat, making it hard to speak or be quiet. They can embarrass you.

What is the cause of hiccups? It has to do with a muscle inside your body called the **diaphragm** (DIE-uh-fram). The diaphragm looks like a rounded dome. It stretches across your chest to help you breathe.

The diaphragm usually works well. It keeps air flowing smoothly in and out of your body. But the diaphragm sometimes gets stuck or irritated and can't work well. It twitches, which interrupts the flow of air. The effect is the hiccups.

Luckily, hiccups are not serious. They usually go away on their own in a short time.

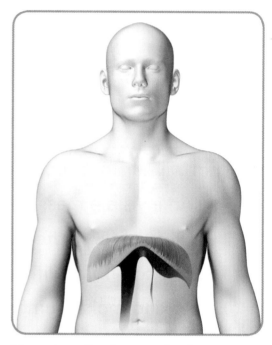

How the diaphragm looks inside the body

Text Marking

Find the cause and effect.

☐	Draw boxes around the signal words **cause** and **effect**.
◯	Circle the cause.
___	<u>Underline</u> the effect.

© Scholastic Inc.

Answer each question. Give details from the article.

1. Which is TRUE about the hiccups?

○ A. Hiccups are caused by too much sleep.

○ B. Hiccups usually go away by themselves.

○ C. Hiccups are a dangerous health problem.

○ D. Hiccups help you breathe smoothly.

What helped you answer? _____

_____

_____

2. The **diaphragm** is a kind of _____.

○ A. muscle   ○ B. illness   ○ C. bone   ○ D. sound

What helped you answer? _____

_____

3. What is the main job of the diaphragm in your body?

_____

_____

4. Why do you think some people feel embarrassed by the hiccups?

_____

_____

No Bones About It

Our bodies contain 206 skeletal bones. Use the symbols to find the medical term for each bone in the diagram. Write it on the line above the common word.

◆ phalanges	● metatarsals	⬟ tarsals	✚ pelvis	✖ metacarpals
✳ clavicle	✦ fibula	★ tibia	✴ patella	O femur
◈ sternum	◻ scapula	◗ cranium	◼ carpals	⬣ ulna and radius
✕ humerus	✲ rib			

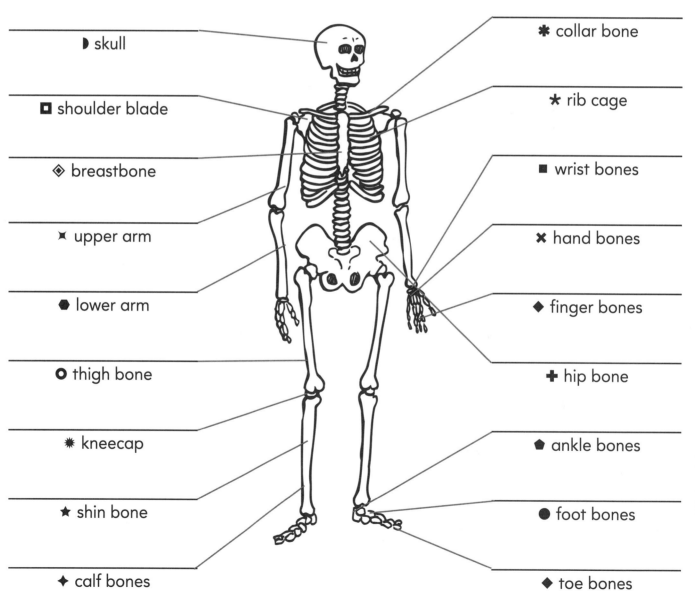

◗ skull

◻ shoulder blade

◈ breastbone

✕ upper arm

⬣ lower arm

O thigh bone

✴ kneecap

★ shin bone

✦ calf bones

✳ collar bone

✲ rib cage

◼ wrist bones

✖ hand bones

◆ finger bones

✚ hip bone

⬟ ankle bones

● foot bones

◆ toe bones

© Scholastic Inc.

ADDITION & SUBTRACTION

Spell It Out

Add. Complete the puzzle using number words.

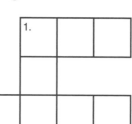

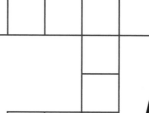

Across

1. 5 + 5 = _____
2. 3 + _____ = 7
3. 2 + _____ = 9
6. 6 + 2 = _____
7. _____ + 0 = 1

Down

1. 4 + _____ = 6
2. 2 + _____ = 7
3. _____ + 4 = 10
4. 4 + 5 = _____
5. 5 + _____ = 8

 Finish each number sentence with a number word.

five + two = _____   three + six = _____

Beautiful Bouquets

Subtract. Draw petals to show the difference.

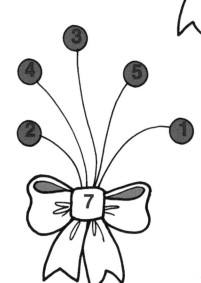

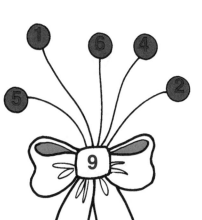

Color the bows with an even number yellow.
Color the bows with an odd number purple.

Crazy Creatures

Add or subtract. Fill in each missing number.

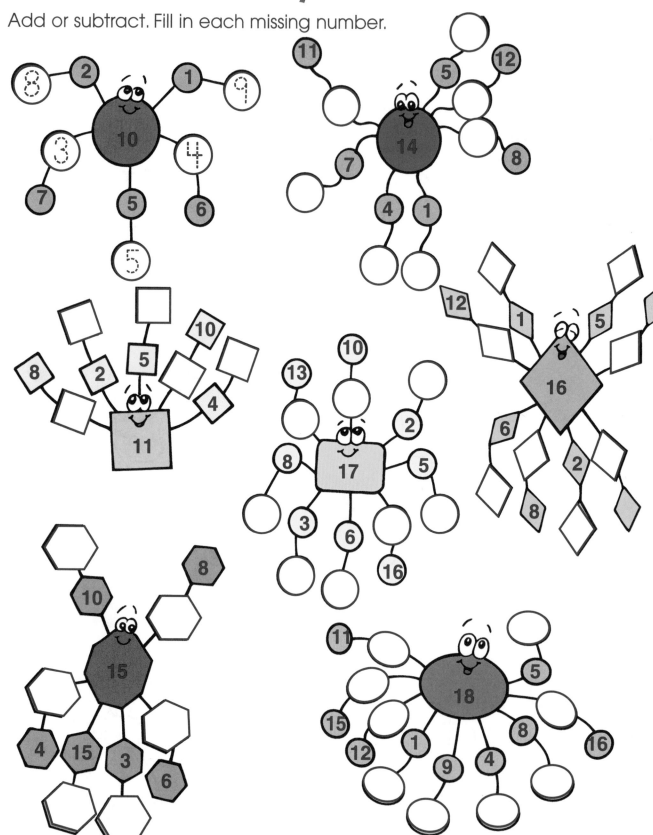

Can You See It?

Write the numbers you see with a . . .

A.  sum of **5** and difference of **1**.

B.  sum of **17** and difference of **7**.

C.  sum of **14** and difference of **2**.

D.  sum of **18** and difference of **4**.

E.  sum of **12** and difference of **2**.

F.  sum of **15** and difference of **9**.

G.  sum of **5** and difference of **3**.

H.  sum of **18** and difference of **2**.

I.  sum of **13** and difference of **5**.

J.  sum of **16** and difference of **6**.

 Make your own number glasses.
sum of _____ and
difference of _____

Scarecrow Sam

Why doesn't Scarecrow Sam tell secrets when he is near Farmer Joe's

bean patch? _____

To find out the answer, add the numbers. Circle the pumpkins that have sums of 14, and write the letters that appear inside those pumpkins in order in the boxes below.

1. 4 + 2   G
2. 7 + 7   B
3. 9 + 5   E
4. 10 + 4   A
5. 4 + 8   R
6. 6 + 8   N
7. 11 + 3   S
8. 14 + 0   T
9. 7 + 2   P
10. 13 + 1   A
11. 5 + 8   S
12. 12 + 2   L
13. 7 + 4   H
14. 5 + 9   K

You've Got Mail!

1. Solve the problems.

2. Find each number pair on the graph. Make a dot for each.

3. Connect the dots in the order that you make them.

4. What picture did you make?

_____

	Across	Up
1.	20 + 7 = _____	12 + 12 = _____
2.	12 + 3 = _____	11 + 13 = _____
3.	1 + 2 = _____	10 + 14 = _____
4.	13 + 2 = _____	10 + 5 = _____
5.	13 + 14 = _____	21 + 3 = _____
6.	23 + 4 = _____	11 + 4 = _____
7.	5 + 22 = _____	2 + 4 = _____
8.	3 + 12 = _____	1 + 5 = _____
9.	3 + 0 = _____	6 + 0 = _____
10.	2 + 1 = _____	2 + 13 = _____
11.	0 + 3 = _____	2 + 22 = _____

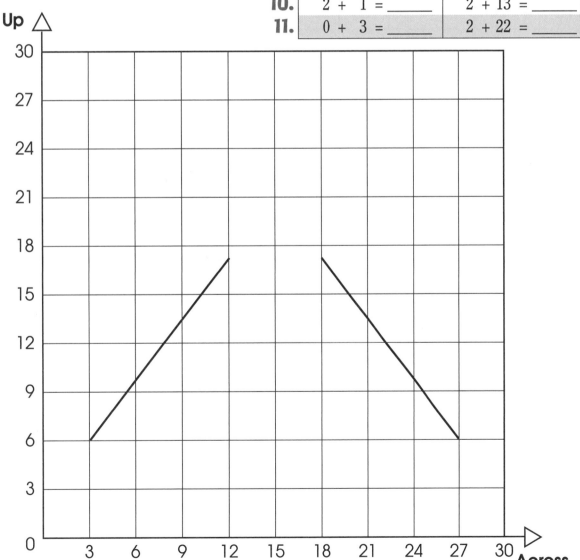

© Scholastic Inc.

Counting on Good Manners

Add. Then use the code to write a letter in
each oval to find the "good manner" words.

11 + 10	62 + 31	44 + 34	41 + 5	13 + 31	35 + 43

◯ ◯ ◯ ◯ ◯ ◯

40 + 10	43 + 24	42 + 4	54 + 25	41 + 42

◯ ◯ ◯ ◯ ◯

57 + 2	22 + 3	34 + 32

◯ ◯ ◯

54 + 5	21 + 4	41 + 25	21 + 11	26 + 52

◯ ◯ ◯ , ◯ ◯

50 + 30	70 + 8	50 + 43	11 + 7	15 + 10	31 + 4	17 + 61

◯ ◯ ◯ ◯ ◯ ◯ ◯

Code

18 C	**21** P	**25** O	**32** R	**35** M	**44** S	**46** A	**50** T
59 Y	**66** U	**67** H	**78** E	**79** N	**80** W	**83** K	**93** L

Just the Same

Add. Connect the flowers with the same sum.

43
+ 26

18
+ 70

11
+ 34

62
+ 35

13
+ 12

52
+ 36

23
+ 22

51
+ 18

14
+ 11

55
+ 42

Make matching sums.

+ _____   + _____   + _____   + _____
78   78   54   54

Planet Earth

Add.

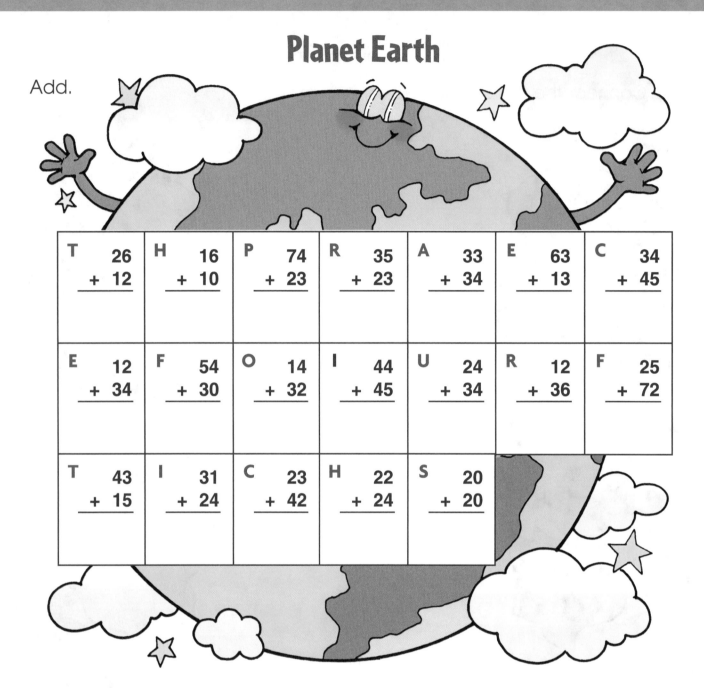

T 26 + 12	**H** 16 + 10	**P** 74 + 23	**R** 35 + 23	**A** 33 + 34	**E** 63 + 13	**C** 34 + 45
E 12 + 34	**F** 54 + 30	**O** 14 + 32	**I** 44 + 45	**U** 24 + 34	**R** 12 + 36	**F** 25 + 72
T 43 + 15	**I** 31 + 24	**C** 23 + 42	**H** 22 + 24	**S** 20 + 20		

For each sum that is an even number, write its letter below in order.

How much of the earth is covered by water?

___ ___ ___ ___ ___ — ___ ___ ___ ___ ___ ___

For each sum that is an odd number, write its letter below in order.

What is the biggest ocean?

___ ___ ___ ___ ___ ___ ___

Let Freedom Ring

Add. Use the code to write words that tell about our past.

63 + 12	12 + 11	65 + 33	62 + 24	34 + 13	24 + 10	41 + 34	53 + 46

◯ ◯ ◯ ◯ ◯ ◯ ◯ ◯

40 + 46	26 + 72	23 + 10	35 + 43	21 + 43	53 + 34	22 + 10	13 + 34	64 + 14	68 + 31

◯ ◯ ◯ ◯ ◯ ◯ ◯ ◯ ◯ ◯

31 + 33	25 + 22	21 + 30	44 + 54	76 + 10	21 + 11	11 + 10

◯ ◯ ◯ ◯ ◯ ◯ ◯

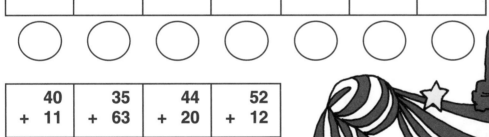

40 + 11	35 + 63	44 + 20	52 + 12

◯ ◯ ◯ ◯

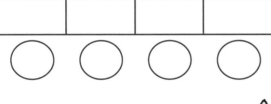

Code

21 Y	**23** M	**32** T	**33** V	**34** C	**42** P	**47** I	**51** B
64 L	**69** D	**75** A	**78** O	**86** R	**87** U	**98** E	**99** N

Detective Work

Use the code to help Detective Dave discover the secret phone number.
The first problem has been done for you.

1	2	3
4	5	6
7	8	9

1.

$$7 - 1 = 6$$

2.

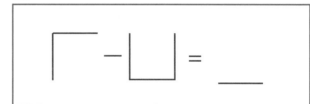

3.

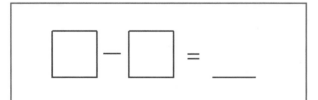

4.

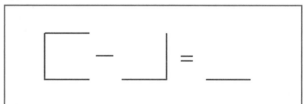

5.

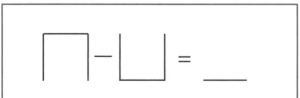

6.

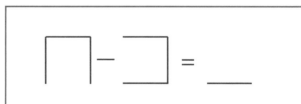

7.

The phone number is:

$$\_\,\_\,\_ - \_\,\_\,\_\,\_$$

© Scholastic Inc.

Chirp, Chirp!

1. Solve the problems.

2. Find each number pair on the graph. Make a dot for each.

3. Connect the dots in the order that you make them.

4. What picture did you make?

_____

	Across	Up
1.	10 − 7 = _____	10 − 8 = _____
2.	4 − 2 = _____	3 − 1 = _____
3.	7 − 5 = _____	1 − 0 = _____
4.	8 − 0 = _____	1 − 0 = _____
5.	9 − 1 = _____	8 − 6 = _____
6.	10 − 3 = _____	7 − 5 = _____
7.	10 − 2 = _____	8 − 2 = _____
8.	8 − 3 = _____	10 − 0 = _____
9.	9 − 7 = _____	7 − 1 = _____
10.	4 − 1 = _____	5 − 3 = _____
11.	9 − 2 = _____	6 − 4 = _____

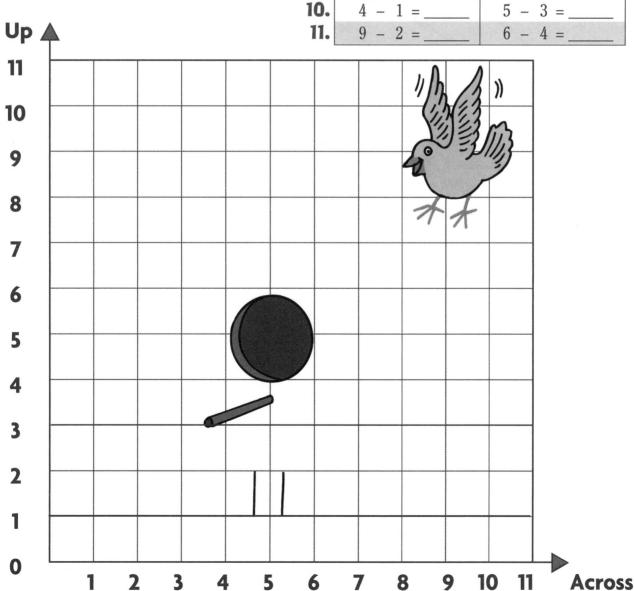

Winter Is Coming

Do the subtraction problems. Help Mr. Squirrel find his way to the tree where he is storing acorns for the winter. Make sure he doesn't cross any odd answers.

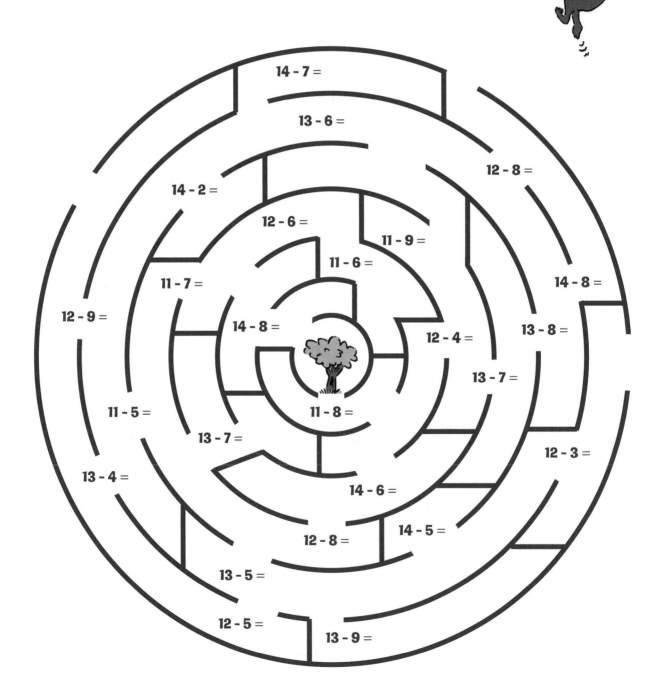

$14 - 7 =$

$13 - 6 =$

$12 - 8 =$

$14 - 2 =$

$12 - 6 =$

$11 - 9 =$

$11 - 6 =$

$11 - 7 =$

$14 - 8 =$

$12 - 9 =$

$14 - 8 =$

$12 - 4 =$

$13 - 8 =$

$13 - 7 =$

$11 - 5 =$

$11 - 8 =$

$13 - 7 =$

$12 - 3 =$

$13 - 4 =$

$14 - 6 =$

$12 - 8 =$

$14 - 5 =$

$13 - 5 =$

$12 - 5 =$

$13 - 9 =$

Baseball Puzzle

What animal can always be found at a baseball game?

To find out, do the subtraction problems. If the answer is greater than 9, color the shapes black. If the answer is less than 10, color the shapes red.

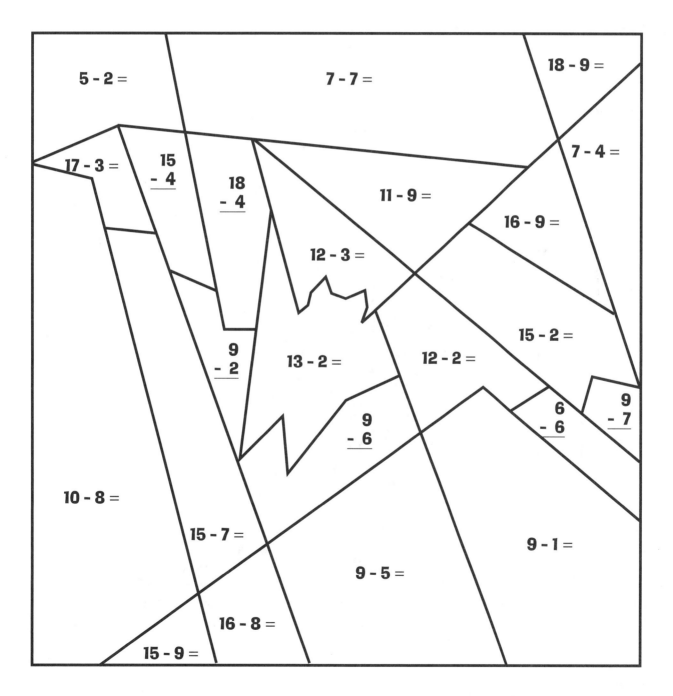

Bubble Yum!

1. Solve the problems.

2. Find each number pair on the graph. Make a dot for each.

3. Connect the dots in the order that you make them.

4. What picture did you make?

_____

	Across	Up
1.	27 – 23 = _____	58 – 53 = _____
2.	18 – 15 = _____	23 – 21 = _____
3.	30 – 27 = _____	29 – 28 = _____
4.	18 – 11 = _____	46 – 45 = _____
5.	58 – 51 = _____	17 – 15 = _____
6.	28 – 22 = _____	49 – 44 = _____
7.	19 – 15 = _____	77 – 72 = _____

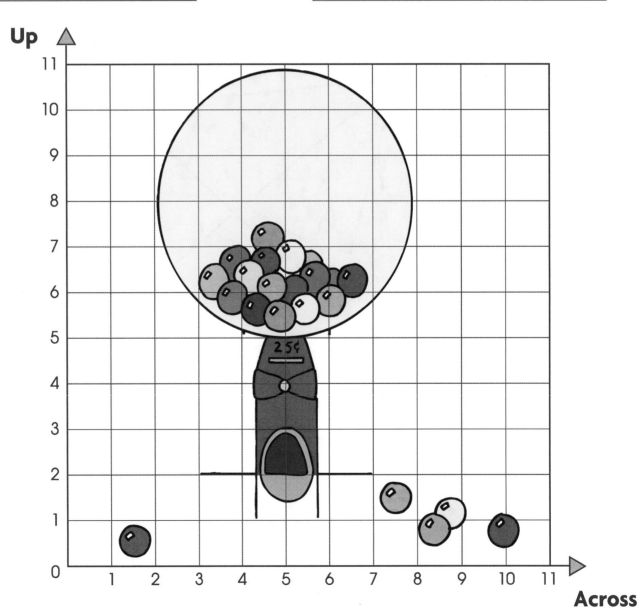

Super Star

Solve the problems. If the answer is between 1 and 20, color the shape red. If the answer is between 21 and 40, color the shape white. If the answer is between 41 and 90, color the shape blue. Taking It Further: Write five subtraction problems that have answers between 10 and 20.

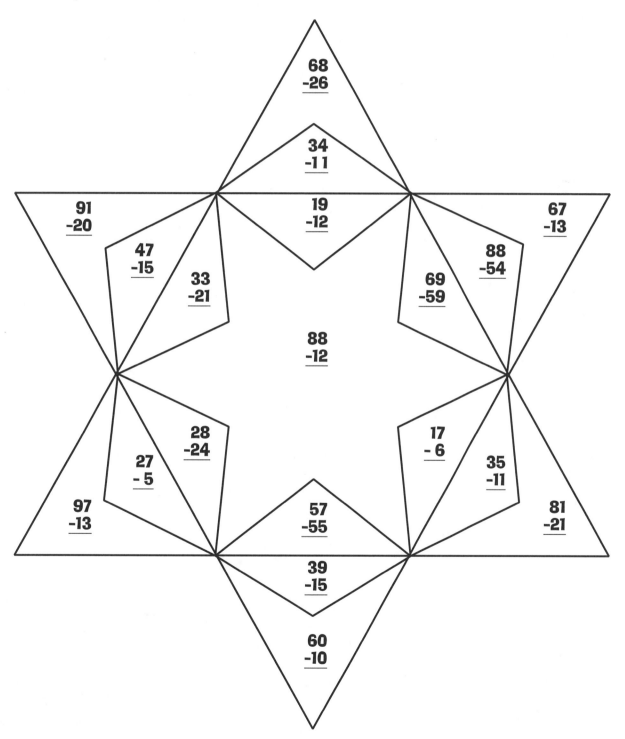

Moving West

Subtract. Follow the even sums to guide the settlers to their new home.

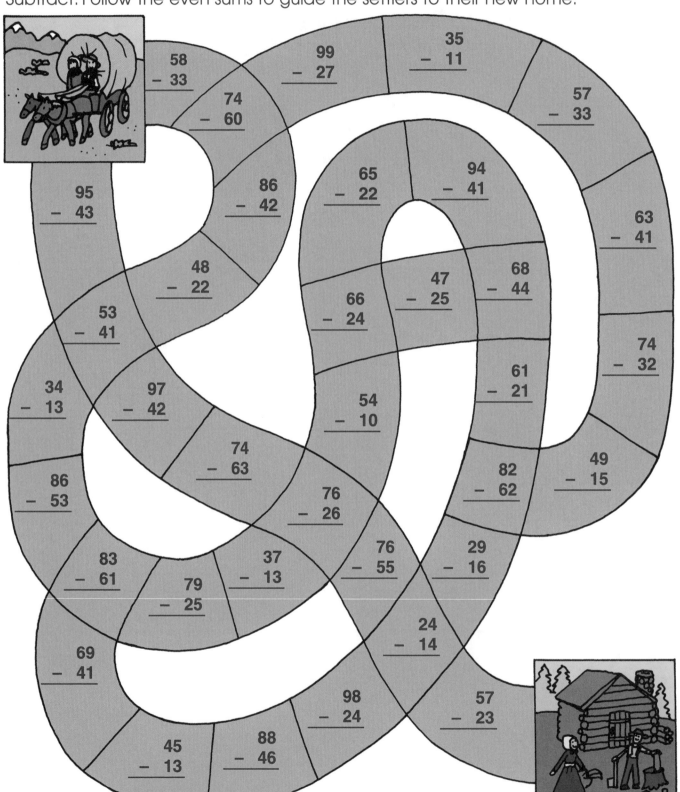

58
− 33

74
− 60

99
− 27

35
− 11

57
− 33

95
− 43

86
− 42

65
− 22

94
− 41

63
− 41

48
− 22

66
− 24

47
− 25

68
− 44

53
− 41

61
− 21

74
− 32

34
− 13

97
− 42

54
− 10

86
− 53

74
− 63

76
− 26

82
− 62

49
− 15

83
− 61

79
− 25

37
− 13

76
− 55

29
− 16

69
− 41

24
− 14

45
− 13

88
− 46

98
− 24

57
− 23

© Scholastic Inc.

High Flying

Subtract.

$$\begin{array}{r} 96 \\ -\ 34 \\ \hline \end{array}$$

$$\begin{array}{r} 59 \\ -\ 26 \\ \hline \end{array}$$

$$\begin{array}{r} 65 \\ -\ 42 \\ \hline \end{array}$$

$$\begin{array}{r} 81 \\ -\ 51 \\ \hline \end{array}$$

$$\begin{array}{r} 43 \\ -\ 22 \\ \hline \end{array}$$

$$\begin{array}{r} 78 \\ -\ 64 \\ \hline \end{array}$$

$$\begin{array}{r} 84 \\ -\ 23 \\ \hline \end{array}$$

$$\begin{array}{r} 37 \\ -\ 15 \\ \hline \end{array}$$

$$\begin{array}{r} 92 \\ -\ 51 \\ \hline \end{array}$$

Color the bird with the smallest number in the ones place red.

Color the bird with the smallest number in the tens place blue.

Color each bird with the same number in the ones and tens place green.

Weather Drops

Subtract. Using the difference in each rain drop, write the weather words in order of their differences from least to greatest by the umbrella handle. Then color your favorite kind of "weather drop" blue.

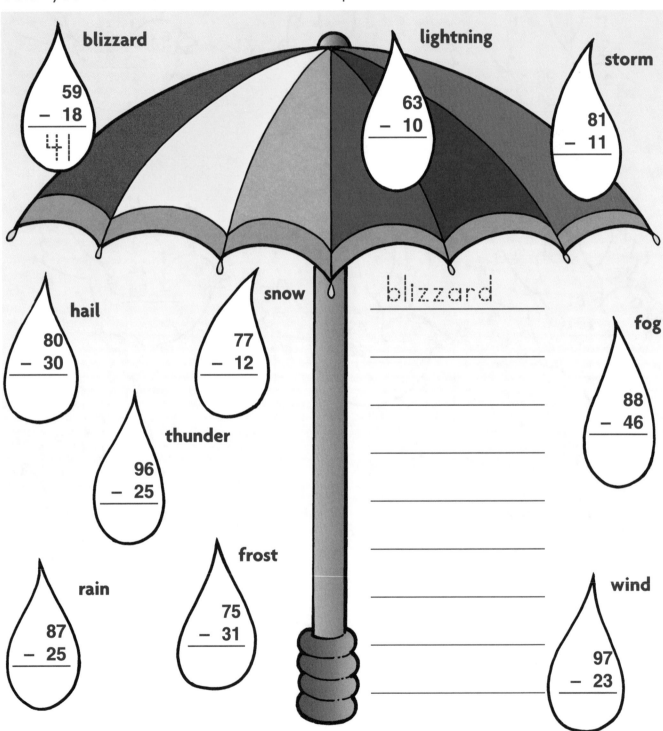

blizzard

$59 - 18 = 41$

lightning

$63 - 10 =$

storm

$81 - 11 =$

hail

$80 - 30 =$

snow

$77 - 12 =$

fog

$88 - 46 =$

thunder

$96 - 25 =$

blizzard

frost

$75 - 31 =$

rain

$87 - 25 =$

wind

$97 - 23 =$

Animal Families

Subtract.

$$\begin{array}{r} 96 \\ -\ 42 \\ \hline \end{array}$$

$$\begin{array}{r} 97 \\ -\ 12 \\ \hline \end{array}$$

$$\begin{array}{r} 86 \\ -\ 43 \\ \hline \end{array}$$

$$\begin{array}{r} 99 \\ -\ 14 \\ \hline \end{array}$$

$$\begin{array}{r} 98 \\ -\ 55 \\ \hline \end{array}$$

$$\begin{array}{r} 78 \\ -\ 24 \\ \hline \end{array}$$

$$\begin{array}{r} 89 \\ -\ 22 \\ \hline \end{array}$$

$$\begin{array}{r} 77 \\ -\ 34 \\ \hline \end{array}$$

$$\begin{array}{r} 78 \\ -\ 11 \\ \hline \end{array}$$

$$\begin{array}{r} 95 \\ -\ 63 \\ \hline \end{array}$$

$$\begin{array}{r} 88 \\ -\ 56 \\ \hline \end{array}$$

Color the animals using the color code.

red	blue	purple	yellow	green
32	43	54	67	85

Triple the Fun

Add. Write the sum on each bowl.

Color bowls with 1, 5, or 8 in the ones place yellow.
Color bowls with 0, 4, or 7 in the ones place pink.
Color bowls with 2, 6, or 9 in the ones place brown.

A Great Catch

Circle each group of 10. Write the number of tens and ones on the chart.
Then write the number on the baseball glove.

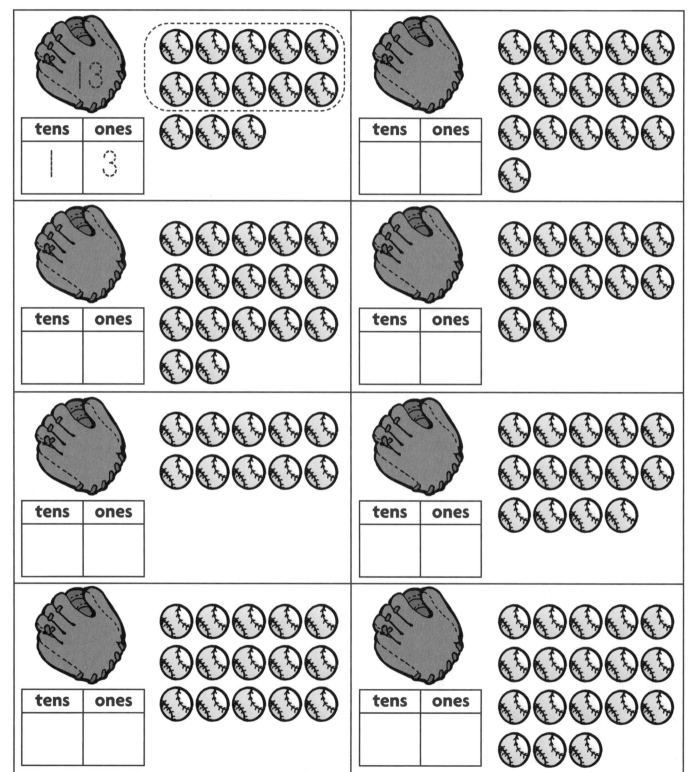

Kaleidoscope

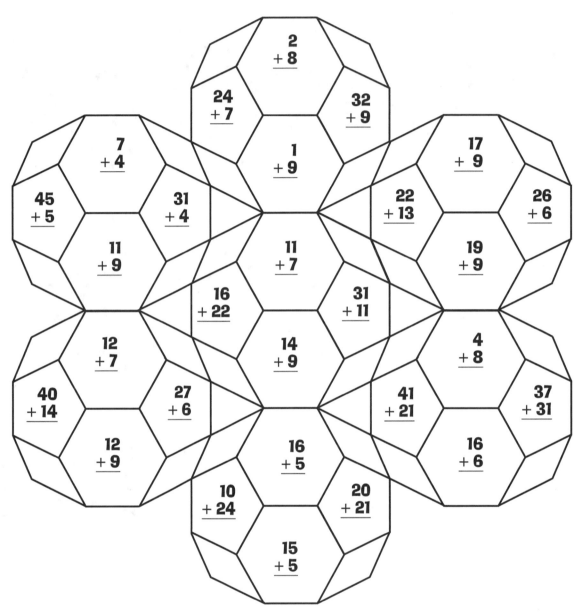

Solve the problems.

If the answer is between 1 and 30, color the shape red.

If the answer is between 31 and 99, color the shape gray.

Finish by coloring the other shapes with the colors of your choice.

Extra: Name two numbers that when added together equal 27.

____ + ____ = ____   ____ + ____ = ____

Zoo Animal

1. Solve the problems.

2. Find each number pair on the graph. Make a dot for each.

3. Connect the dots in the order that you make them.

4. What picture did you make?

_____

	Across	**Up**
1.	13 + 7 = _____	12 + 4 = _____
2.	15 + 9 = _____	5 + 3 = _____
3.	11 + 9 = _____	0 + 4 = _____
4.	19 + 9 = _____	2 + 2 = _____
5.	10 + 18 = _____	11 + 5 = _____
6.	16 + 16 = _____	9 + 7 = _____
7.	28 + 8 = _____	2 + 6 = _____

	Across	**Up**
8.	17 + 15 = _____	1 + 3 = _____
9.	31 + 9 = _____	3 + 1 = _____
10.	8 + 32 = _____	8 + 8 = _____
11.	19 + 25 = _____	19 + 1 = _____
12.	27 + 17 = _____	18 + 14 = _____
13.	7 + 29 = _____	17 + 23 = _____
14.	18 + 6 = _____	25 + 15 = _____

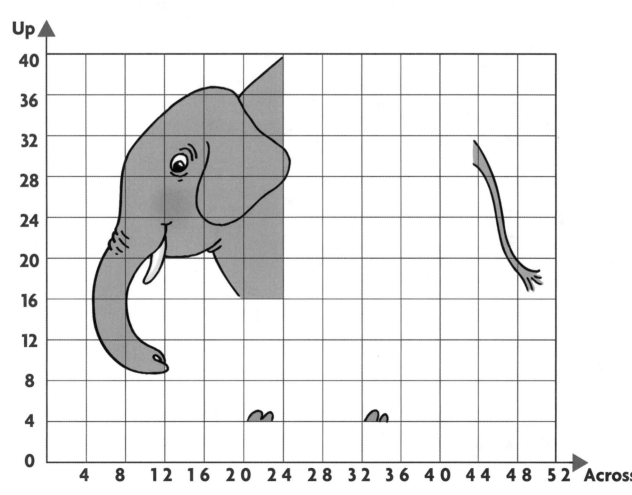

© Scholastic Inc.

Don't Forget Your Keys

Add. Then follow the clue to find the right key. Write the sum in the key hole.

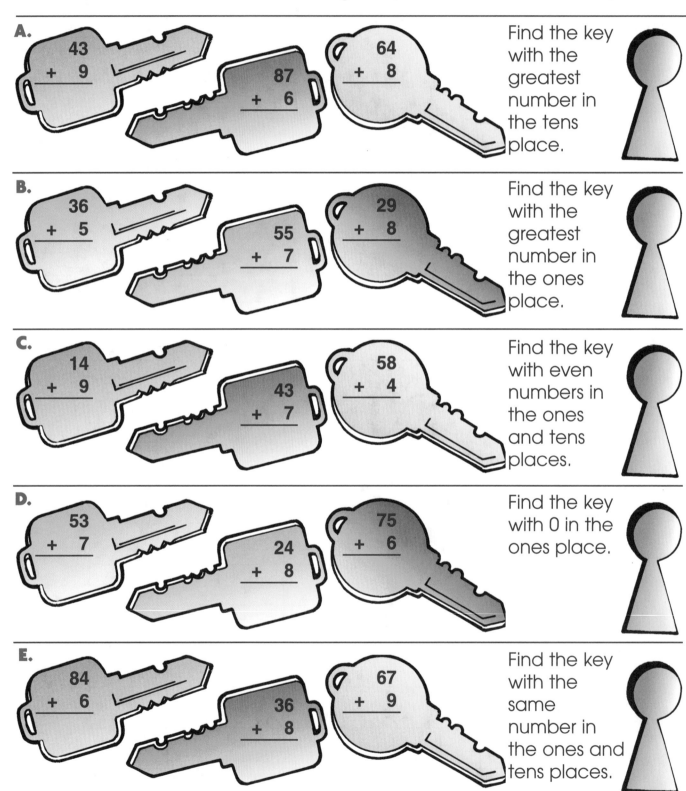

A.
```
  43
+  9
```
```
  87
+  6
```
```
  64
+  8
```
Find the key with the greatest number in the tens place.

B.
```
  36
+  5
```
```
  55
+  7
```
```
  29
+  8
```
Find the key with the greatest number in the ones place.

C.
```
  14
+  9
```
```
  43
+  7
```
```
  58
+  4
```
Find the key with even numbers in the ones and tens places.

D.
```
  53
+  7
```
```
  24
+  8
```
```
  75
+  6
```
Find the key with 0 in the ones place.

E.
```
  84
+  6
```
```
  36
+  8
```
```
  67
+  9
```
Find the key with the same number in the ones and tens places.

Treasure of a Book

Add. Then color each box with an odd sum to help the boy find his way to the book. Hint: Remember to look in the ones place.

47 + 24	74 + 19	78 + 12	15 + 37
48 + 44	31 + 59	52 + 39	29 + 57	73 + 19
63 + 18	14 + 67	57 + 16	24 + 18	63 + 29
57 + 28	27 + 47	76 + 16	72 + 18	76 + 18
32 + 19	17 + 24	55 + 38	32 + 49	

How Do We Get There?

49 miles

32 miles

54 miles

31 miles

MOUNTAINS

BEACH

25 miles

13 miles

48 miles

88 miles

17 miles

10 miles

28 miles

39 miles

Add the distance of each route from the house to the beach.

Route #1   Route #2

___   ___

___   ___

___   ___

+ ___   + ___

_____   _____
miles   miles

Add the distance of each route from the house to the mountains.

Route #1   Route #2

___   ___

___   ___

___   ___

+ ___   + ___

_____   _____
miles   miles

Crossdigit Wiz

Find the sums of the three addends in the rows across and down.
The answer circles are numbered.

You can do it!

	8	6	7	◯ 1.
13	8	5	◯ 2.		5
7	4	3	◯ 3.	4.	10

8 16 7 ◯ 20

9 ◯ 5.

30 10 4 9 15 ◯

21 7. ◯ 6 6.

7 16 5 8 ◯ 8.

11

◯ 9. ◯ 10.

© Scholastic Inc.

Carnival Fun

Do the problems below. Then find your answers hidden in the carnival scene and circle them. Can you find all twelve answers?

$$
\begin{array}{r} 15 \\ 33 \\ + 27 \\ \hline \end{array}
\qquad
\begin{array}{r} 27 \\ 23 \\ + 12 \\ \hline \end{array}
\qquad
\begin{array}{r} 34 \\ 23 \\ + 24 \\ \hline \end{array}
\qquad
\begin{array}{r} 15 \\ 25 \\ + 10 \\ \hline \end{array}
\qquad
\begin{array}{r} 16 \\ 14 \\ + 14 \\ \hline \end{array}
\qquad
\begin{array}{r} 12 \\ 31 \\ + 17 \\ \hline \end{array}
$$

$$
\begin{array}{r} 28 \\ 22 \\ + 45 \\ \hline \end{array}
\qquad
\begin{array}{r} 43 \\ 27 \\ + 27 \\ \hline \end{array}
\qquad
\begin{array}{r} 10 \\ 17 \\ + 18 \\ \hline \end{array}
\qquad
\begin{array}{r} 29 \\ 13 \\ + 16 \\ \hline \end{array}
\qquad
\begin{array}{r} 37 \\ 31 \\ + 17 \\ \hline \end{array}
\qquad
\begin{array}{r} 51 \\ 23 \\ + 17 \\ \hline \end{array}
$$

Crack the Numbers

Look at the number on each chick. Write the number of tens and ones on the egg. Then trade one ten for ten ones.

35
_3_ tens   _5_ ones

_2_ tens
_15_ ones

47
___ tens   ___ ones

___ tens
___ ones

82
___ tens   ___ ones

___ tens
___ ones

94
___ tens   ___ ones

___ tens
___ ones

61
___ tens   ___ ones

___ tens
___ ones

90
___ tens   ___ ones

___ tens
___ ones

Digging Up Bones

Help Daisy find a delicious bone! Subtract.
Circle the answer that goes with each bone.

> is greater than and < is less than

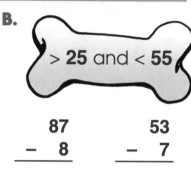

A.

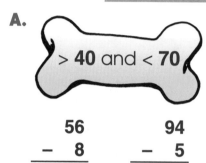

> **40** and < **70**

56	94
− 8	− 5

B.

> **25** and < **55**

87	53
− 8	− 7

C.

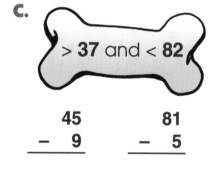

> **37** and < **82**

45	81
− 9	− 5

D.

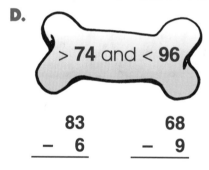

> **74** and < **96**

83	68
− 6	− 9

E.

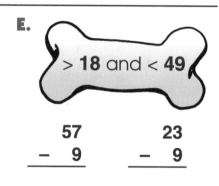

> **18** and < **49**

57	23
− 9	− 9

F.

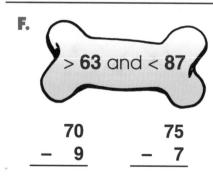

> **63** and < **87**

70	75
− 9	− 7

G.

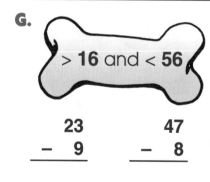

> **16** and < **56**

23	47
− 9	− 8

 Write two subtraction problems on another piece of paper. One answer should match the bone.

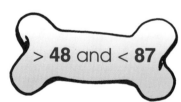

> **48** and < **87**

First, Next, Last

Subtract. Then number the pictures in order from least to greatest.

A.

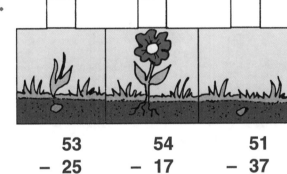

64	58	83
− 45	− 19	− 46

B.

83	24	28
− 75	− 18	− 19

C.

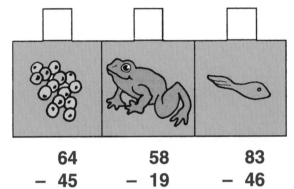

53	54	51
− 25	− 17	− 37

D.

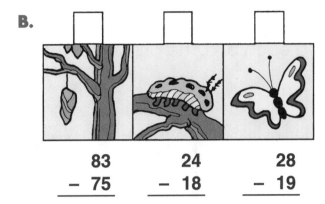

88	91	82
− 59	− 53	− 45

E.

73	71	76
− 44	− 35	− 28

F.

82	34	57
− 64	− 19	− 38

© Scholastic Inc.

Purdy Bird

Purdy the Parakeet loves to look at herself in the mirror. Only one of these parakeets below really shows what Purdy looks like in the mirror. Can you find the right one? To check your answer, do the subtraction problems next to each bird. The answer for the correct bird is 24.

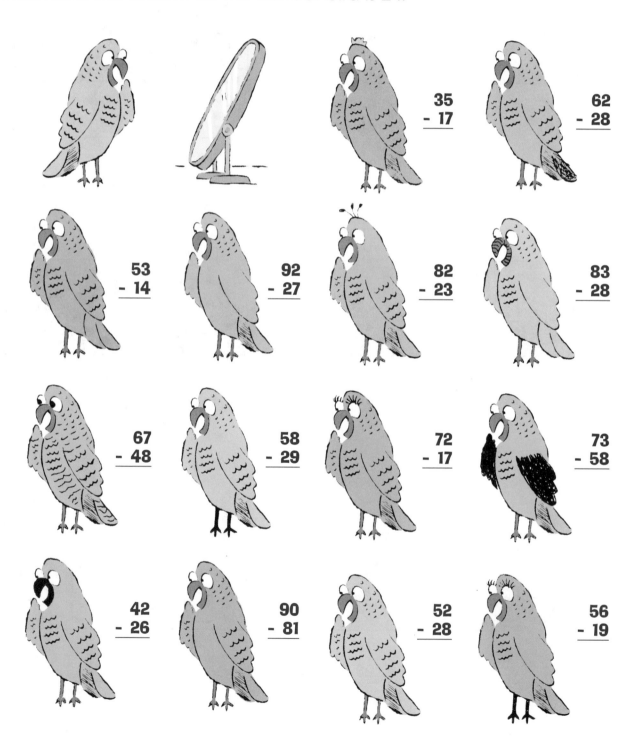

$$35 - 17$$

$$62 - 28$$

$$53 - 14$$

$$92 - 27$$

$$82 - 23$$

$$83 - 28$$

$$67 - 48$$

$$58 - 29$$

$$72 - 17$$

$$73 - 58$$

$$42 - 26$$

$$90 - 81$$

$$52 - 28$$

$$56 - 19$$

Grandma's Quilt

Solve the problems. If the answer is between 1 and 50, color the shape red. If the answer is between 51 and 100, color the shape blue. Finish the design by coloring the other shapes with the colors of your choice.

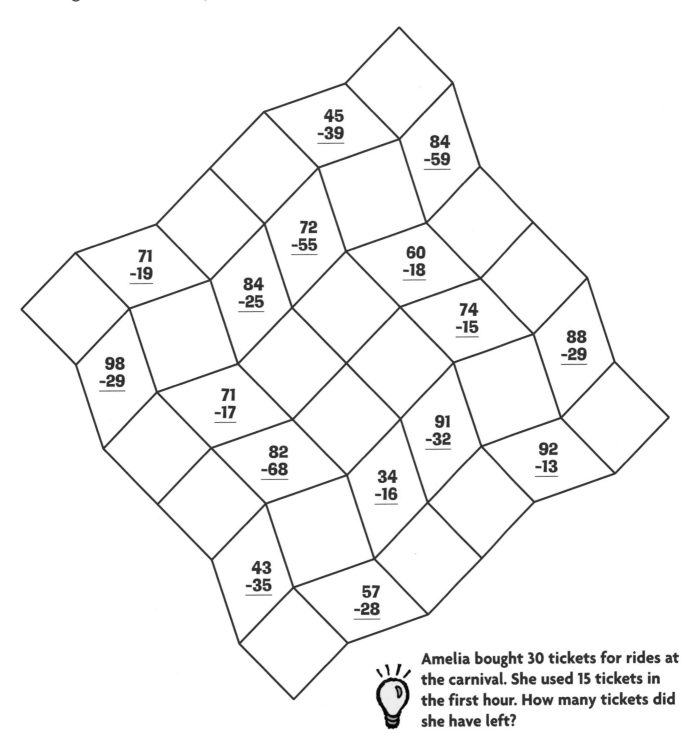

Amelia bought 30 tickets for rides at the carnival. She used 15 tickets in the first hour. How many tickets did she have left?

All Tied Up

Subtract. Add to check.

$$\begin{array}{r} 65 \\ -\ 27 \\ \hline 38 \end{array}$$

$$\begin{array}{r} 38 \\ +\ 27 \\ \hline 65 \end{array}$$

$$\begin{array}{r} 77 \\ -\ 38 \\ \hline \end{array}$$

$$+\ \rule{2cm}{0.4pt}$$

$$\begin{array}{r} 24 \\ -\ 15 \\ \hline \end{array}$$

$$+\ \rule{2cm}{0.4pt}$$

$$\begin{array}{r} 32 \\ -\ 13 \\ \hline \end{array}$$

$$+\ \rule{2cm}{0.4pt}$$

$$\begin{array}{r} 83 \\ -\ 49 \\ \hline \end{array}$$

$$+\ \rule{2cm}{0.4pt}$$

$$\begin{array}{r} 50 \\ -\ 19 \\ \hline \end{array}$$

$$+\ \rule{2cm}{0.4pt}$$

$$\begin{array}{r} 46 \\ -\ 29 \\ \hline \end{array}$$

$$+\ \rule{2cm}{0.4pt}$$

$$\begin{array}{r} 62 \\ -\ 15 \\ \hline \end{array}$$

$$+\ \rule{2cm}{0.4pt}$$

Write your own subtraction problem. Add to check.

$$-\ \rule{2cm}{0.4pt}$$

$$+\ \rule{2cm}{0.4pt}$$

Teenie Tiny Babies

Add or subtract.

U.   42
   + 39

L.   53
   − 48

N.   31
   + 29

C.   74
   − 28

O.   44
   + 46

P.   75
   − 37

H.   40
   − 17

K.   27
   + 36

S.   96
   − 48

A.   62
   − 48

G.   80
   − 62

M.   55
   + 16

R.   88
   − 19

Write the letter that goes with each number.

I am smaller than your
thumb when I'm born. ___ ___ ___ ___ ___ ___ ___ ___
                      63 14 60 18 14 69 90 90

I am even smaller. ___ ___ ___ ___ ___
                    63 90 14   5 14

I am smaller than a bumblebee. ___ ___ ___ ___ ___ ___ ___
                                90 38 90 48 48 81 71

Since we are so little, we
live right next to our mothers in a safe, warm ___ ___ ___ ___ ___ .
                                                38 90 81 46 23

Day by Day

Add or subtract. Color each special date on the calendar.

| | | | July | | | |
Sun.	Mon.	Tues.	Wed.	Thur.	Fri.	Sat.
		1	2	3	4	5
6	7	8	9	10	11	12
13	14	15	16	17	18	19
20	21	22	23	24	25	26
27	28	29	30	31		

A. Camp begins one week after the second Monday. Color this date red.

B. The baseball game is two weeks before the fourth Wednesday. Color this date green.

C. The birthday party is two weeks after the second Saturday. Color this date purple.

D. The swim meet is three weeks before the fifth Tuesday. Color this date blue.

E. The trip to the zoo is one week before the third Sunday. Color this date orange.

F. The picnic is two weeks before the fifth Thursday. Color this date yellow.

G. What date is 14 days after the third Wednesday? Color this date pink.

H. What date is 18 days before the fourth Friday? Color this date brown.

Pizza Vote

Use the circle graph to compare the results of the pizza vote.

A. How many students voted for pepperoni and cheese in all?

B. How many more students voted for cheese than veggie?

C. How many more students voted for pepperoni than sausage?

D. How many students voted for mushroom and veggie altogether?

E. How many more students voted for mushroom than veggie?

F. How many students voted for sausage and pepperoni in all?

G. How many students voted for veggie, cheese, and mushroom in all?

 Find the total number of students who voted.

Tool Time

Find the sum of the numbers in each tool.

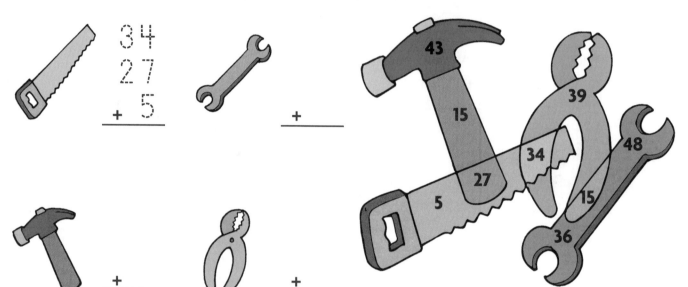

```
  3 4
  2 7
+   5
-----
```

+ _____

+ _____   + _____

A. Write the number found in the 🔨 and 🪚 .

Write the number found in the 🔧 and 🗜 .

Find the sum.

```
┌─────┐
│     │
└─────┘
┌─────┐
│     │
└─────┘
+
─────────
```

B. Find the difference between the largest and smallest numbers in each tool.

_____ − _____   _____ − _____   _____ − _____   _____ − _____

 On another piece of paper, find the sum of the tools altogether.
Hint: You'll be adding nine numbers.

Powerful Presidents

Add. Color each even sum red to learn about George Washington. Color each odd sum blue to learn about Abe Lincoln. Hint: Look in the ones place.

A. the "Father of the Country"

```
  423
+ 173
```

B. born in 1809 in Kentucky

```
  384
+ 611
```

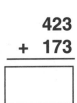

C. sixteenth president

```
  325
+ 552
```

D. 6 feet 4 inches tall

```
  257
+ 312
```

E. born in 1732 in Virginia

```
  101
+ 561
```

F. studied geography

```
  570
+ 408
```

G. first president

```
  805
+ 163
```

H. leader in the Revolutionary War

```
  445
+ 151
```

I. loved reading books

```
  609
+ 290
```

J. leader in the Civil War

```
  314
+ 183
```

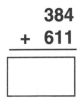

Hundreds of Pumpkins

Regroup tens into hundreds. Remember: 10 tens = 1 hundred. Write the number of hundreds and the number of remaining tens.

27 tens
__2__ hundreds
__7__ tens

84 tens
____ hundreds
____ tens

93 tens
____ hundreds
____ tens

71 tens
____ hundreds
____ tens

56 tens
____ hundreds
____ tens

32 tens
____ hundreds
____ tens

49 tens
____ hundreds
____ tens

65 tens
____ hundreds
____ tens

Write the number.

5 hundreds **7 tens** **0 ones**

8 hundreds **0 tens** **4 ones**

© Scholastic Inc.

Through the Tunnels

Add. Then trace the mole's path to the top. The mole must travel through tunnels with a zero in the sum.

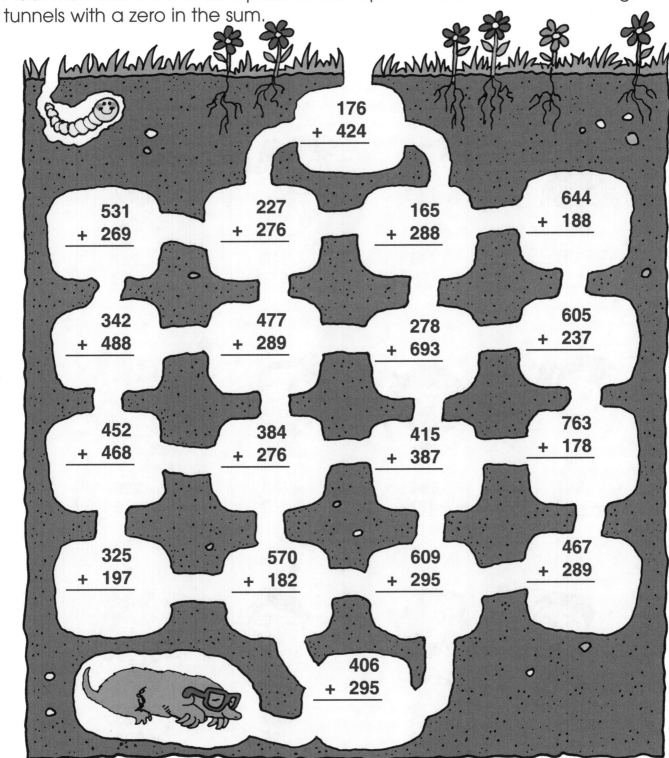

$$176 + 424$$

$$531 + 269 \qquad 227 + 276 \qquad 165 + 288 \qquad 644 + 188$$

$$342 + 488 \qquad 477 + 289 \qquad 278 + 693 \qquad 605 + 237$$

$$452 + 468 \qquad 384 + 276 \qquad 415 + 387 \qquad 763 + 178$$

$$325 + 197 \qquad 570 + 182 \qquad 609 + 295 \qquad 467 + 289$$

$$406 + 295$$

On another piece of paper, write three more problems that have a zero in the sum.

Tricky Twins

Sandy and Mandy are having a twin party. There are six sets of twins, but only one set of identical twins. To find the identical twins, solve the addition problems under each person. The identical twins have the same answer.

$$207 \atop + \ 545$$ $$126 \atop + \ \ 89$$ $$328 \atop + \ 347$$ $$257 \atop + \ 458$$

$$547 \atop + \ 129$$ $$624 \atop + \ 127$$ $$108 \atop + \ 107$$ $$229 \atop + \ 418$$

$$258 \atop + \ 268$$ $$389 \atop + \ 336$$ $$417 \atop + \ 129$$ $$253 \atop + \ 494$$

Eager Leader

Fill in the missing numbers.

```
  2 [ ] 8          4 0 [ ]
+ [ ] 5 [ ]      + 3 [ ] 5
  ─────────        ─────────
  6   7   9        [ ] 1   8
```

```
  2 [ ] 7          3 [ ] [ ]        1 2 5
+ [ ] 5 [ ]      + 1   2   4      + [ ] [ ] [ ]
  ─────────        ─────────        ─────────
  3   9   8        [ ] 7   8        4   7   9
```

How are you doing?

```
  1 5 [ ]                           5 [ ] 8
+ [ ] 3 [ ] 2                     + [ ] 6 [ ]
  ─────────                         ─────────
  [ ] 9   2                         7   6   9
```

```
  4 [ ] [ ]        1 4 6            3 1 4
+ 2   2   0      + [ ] 3 [ ]      + [ ] [ ] [ ]
  ─────────        ─────────        ─────────
  [ ] 7   9        3 [ ] 8          4   3   7
```

Sandwich Shop

Menu

hot dog	$1.53	fruit salad	$1.90
pbj	$1.49	veggies & dip	$1.84
turkey sub	$1.86	chips	$ .50
hamburger	$1.72	fries	$ .65
juice	$ .84	cupcake	$1.07
milk	$ .75	brownie	$1.22
shake	$1.17	cookies	$ .86

Add.

A.

pbj
chips
milk
brownie   +
_____

B.

hamburger
fries
shake   +
_____

C.

turkey sub
veggies & dip
juice
cupcake   +
_____

D.

hot dog
fruit salad
brownie
juice   +
_____

E.

turkey sub
chips
shake   +
_____

F.

pbj
cookies
milk   +
_____

Easy as 1, 2, 3

Add to find the perimeter of each shape.

A.

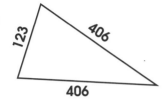

123
406
406

B.

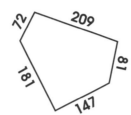

209
72
181
147
81

C.

146
82
266
139
120

```
  1 2 3
  4 0 6
+ 4 0 6
```

+ _____

+ _____

D.

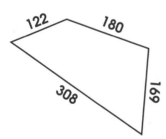

122
180
308
169

E.

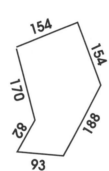

154
154
170
188
82
93

F.

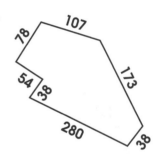

78
107
54 38
173
280
38

+ _____

+ _____

+ _____

Color each shape using the code below.

9 hundreds — orange	4 tens — red	3 ones — purple
6 hundreds — green	7 tens — yellow	8 ones — blue

Count Down

Regroup hundreds to tens. Remember: 1 hundred = 10 tens.

The Sun's Family

Draw a line to each matching difference to connect each planet to a fact about it.

Mars

694
− 421

Saturn

935
− 123

Mercury

573
− 241

Jupiter

937
− 304

Earth

437
− 225

Uranus

968
− 413

397
− 185
I am a ball of rock and metal but covered with soil, rock, and water.

982
− 650
I am a bare, rocky ball similar to Earth's moon.

847
− 214
I am the largest planet in our solar system.

963
− 151
I am surrounded by seven flat rings made of pieces of ice.

857
− 302
I am a planet with 27 known moons.

596
− 323
I am called the Red Planet.

A Place in Space

Draw a line to each matching difference to connect each planet or space object to a fact about it.

Venus	
	713 − 171

Neptune	
	833 − 117

Sun	
	675 − 216

Moon	
	407 − 223

Comet	
	514 − 126

952 − 236	I am a planet with days lasting only 16 hours.
857 − 469	I am like a dirty snowball made of dust, ice, and gases.
612 − 428	I am covered with craters.
931 − 389	I am sizzling hot with no water.
892 − 433	I am the star closest to Earth.

 Complete each pattern. Then tell someone the pattern for each set of numbers.

900, 800, 700, _____, _____, _____, _____, _____, _____

900, 700, 500, _____, _____

800, 600, 400, _____

Tricky Zero

Subtract.

480
− 136

360
− 318

190
− 124

720
− 517

502
− 289

208
− 129

904
− 435

500
− 247

490
− 256

800
− 643

305
− 176

300
− 134

700
− 391

Treasures Under the Sea

Add or subtract. Use the chart to color the picture.

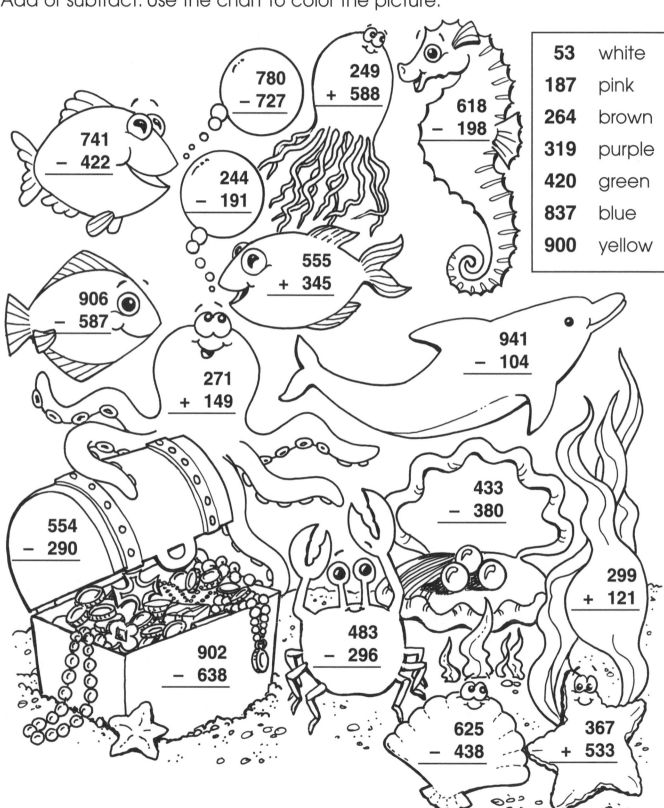

53	white
187	pink
264	brown
319	purple
420	green
837	blue
900	yellow

780
− 727

249
+ 588

618
− 198

741
− 422

244
− 191

555
+ 345

906
− 587

941
− 104

271
+ 149

554
− 290

433
− 380

299
+ 121

902
− 638

483
− 296

625
− 438

367
+ 533

© Scholastic Inc.

Follow the Trees

Add or subtract. Then trace the bear's path to its cave. The bear follows trees with sums that have a 3 in the tens place.

$$687 + 143$$

$$584 - 146$$

$$727 + 204$$

$$364 - 125$$

$$148 + 132$$

$$952 - 219$$

$$497 + 236$$

$$486 + 250$$

$$845 - 486$$

$$470 + 289$$

$$657 - 594$$

$$604 - 266$$

CAVE, SWEET CAVE

School Supplies

markers
folders
scissors
glue sticks
pencils

	100	200	300	400	500	600	700	800	900

Add or subtract. Use the graph to help solve each problem.

A. Mrs. Randolph's class used 523 pencils. How many are left?

B. Mr. Kirk's class used 156 scissors. How many are left?

C. Mr. Dean's class took 248 folders. Mr. Jordan's class took 176 folders. How many did they take altogether?

How many folders are left?

D. Mrs. Fenton's class used 96 glue sticks. Mrs. McBride's class used 189 glue sticks. How many did they use altogether?

How many glue sticks are left?

E. Mrs. Barry's class needs 275 markers. Mr. Lopez's class needs 398 markers. How many do they need altogether?

How many markers are left?

Movie Madness

Add or subtract to solve.

A. 168 people are in line to buy tickets. 159 seats are available in the theater. How many people will not get a ticket to the movie?

B. 427 people attended the rush hour show. 289 people attended the 7:00 show. How many attended both shows altogether?

C. 507 people ordered a popcorn and a soda. 278 people ordered popcorn only. How many more people ordered a soda?

D. 319 people bought a pretzel. 299 people bought a box of candy. How many pretzels and candy were sold altogether?

E. There were 826 people at the movie theater on Friday. On Saturday, there were 697 people. How many more people were at the movie theater on Friday?

F. 258 people ordered a hot dog with mustard. 273 people ordered a hot dog with ketchup. How many hot dogs were ordered in all?

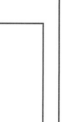

Animal Facts

Add or subtract.

T 247 + 253	**O** 463 + 440	**L** 217 + 68	**P** 639 + 207	**A** 391 + 144	**W** 459 + 492	**I** 198 + 672
P 842 − 314	**L** 504 + 475	**I** 500 − 293	**R** 457 + 364	**I** 903 − 339	**O** 107 + 147	**A** 924 − 71
N 700 − 427	**N** 903 − 34	**R** 703 − 186	**H** 258 + 553	**A** 357 + 537		

Move across each row. Write
the letter from each box with
the correct number of
hundreds.

 2 hundreds   I am a cat that likes to sleep 20 hours a day.

5 hundreds   I have four toes on my front feet and three toes on my back feet.

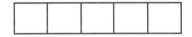

8 hundreds   I am a fish with razor-sharp teeth.

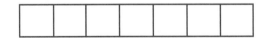

9 hundreds   I can see well at night but cannot move my eyes.

Very Special Helpers

Add or subtract. Write the letter that goes with each answer in the center.

	E	**L**	**H**	**F**	**D**	**A**
207 + 566	814 − 245	339 + 128	540 − 166	422 − 174	615 − 230	409 + 387

772 − 484

596 + 287

600 − 341

603 + 197

I 635 + 199

M 841 − 152

T 478 + 418

P 416 + 288

248 834 800 569 689 796 288

896 569 796 259 374 569 800

385 883 259 896 883 800

467 834 773 800 796 800 834 796 288

704 883 467 834 259 569 689 796 288

Vacation Time

Write the name and the price of each item in the correct suitcase. Add the prices.

$.77

$7.14

$2.10

$6.89

$1.23

$1.23

$3.74

$1.46

Beach

$ _____
$ _____
$ _____
$ _____
Total $ _____

Mountains

$ _____
$ _____
$ _____
$ _____
Total $ _____

How much more does it cost to fill the mountain suitcase than the beach suitcase? Show your work on another piece of paper.

© Scholastic Inc.

Bull's-eye

Select any problem. Add or subtract. Color the answer on the target. Repeat
until you hit the bull's-eye. Then answer the remaining problems.

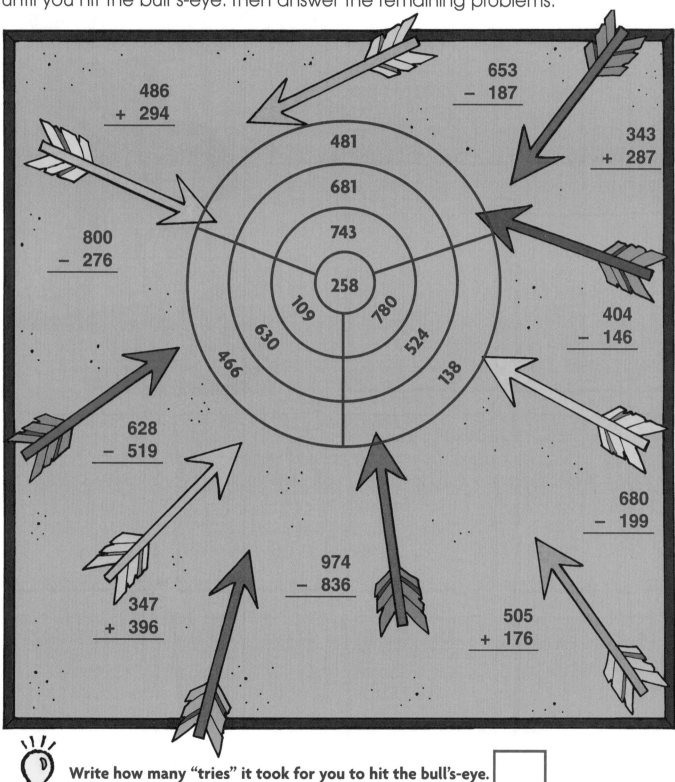

653
− 187

486
+ 294

343
+ 287

481

681

743

800
− 276

258

109   780

630   524

466   138

404
− 146

628
− 519

680
− 199

347
+ 396

974
− 836

505
+ 176

Write how many "tries" it took for you to hit the bull's-eye.

Grid Math

	A	B	C	D
3	550	636	282	963
2	189	148	579	415
1	427	751	370	804

Find the numbers on the grid. Add or subtract.

(A, 1) + (C, 3)

(B, 3) – (A, 3)

(D, 3) – (A, 2)

(B, 2) + (C, 1)

(A, 3) + (C, 1)

(D, 1) – (B, 3)

(A, 2) + (B, 1)

(C, 2) – (C, 3)

(D, 3) – (B, 2)

(D, 2) + (A, 2)

© Scholastic Inc.

Perfect Punt

Add or subtract. Draw a line to connect each football to its goalpost.

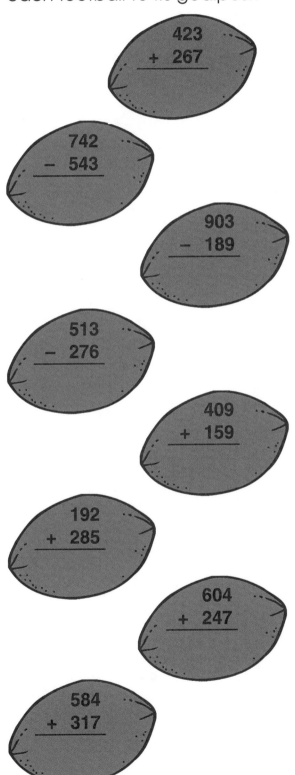

$$423 + 267$$

$$742 - 543$$

$$903 - 189$$

$$513 - 276$$

$$409 + 159$$

$$192 + 285$$

$$604 + 247$$

$$584 + 317$$

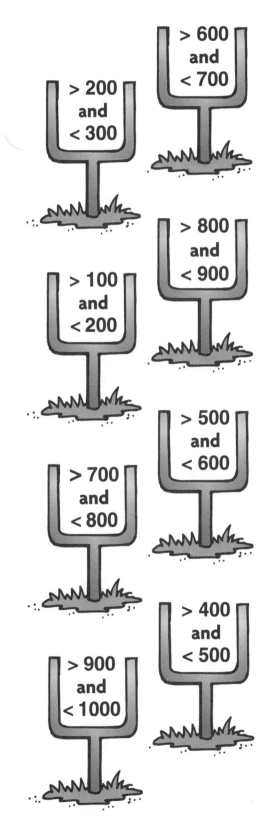

> 200 and < 300

> 600 and < 700

> 100 and < 200

> 800 and < 900

> 700 and < 800

> 500 and < 600

> 900 and < 1000

> 400 and < 500

Tic-Tac-Toe

How to Play:

1. Solve the problems in the first row of a game.

2. Mark the gameboard with an X or O for the largest answer.

3. Continue to solve the problems in each row to try to get three in a row.

Game 1

X	O
374 + 263	429 + 187
154 + 199	740 − 286
643 + 208	341 + 459
973 − 784	514 − 188
291 + 263	445 + 375

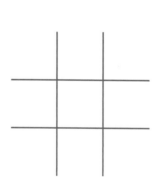

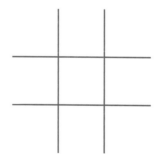

Game 2

X	O
166 + 117	149 + 69
801 − 389	722 − 305
318 + 218	266 + 243
576 + 268	607 + 266
629 − 457	785 − 657

© Scholastic Inc.

Scholastic Success With

MATH

Lone Donor

This is a number line. The numbers increase as you go along the line.

Write the missing numbers.

Mystery Critter

I climb up the side of walls and never fall.
I am a fast runner and have a very long tail. Who am I? _____

To find out, connect the numbers in order from 20 to 68.

Order Recorder

Write the missing numbers.

1. 64, 65, 66, _____

2. 33, _____, _____

3. 41, _____, _____, 44

4. 15, _____, 17, _____, 19

5. _____, _____, _____, 76

6. 29, 30, _____, _____, 33

Write what comes next.

7. 2   4   5   6   _____ _____ _____ _____

8. 3   6   9   12   _____ _____ _____ _____

Write the numbers between 82 and 89.

9. 82 _____, _____, _____, _____, _____, _____, 89

Write **before** or **after**.

10. Room 479 comes _____ room 478.

11. Page 53 comes _____ page 63.

12. 15th street comes _____ 12th street.

13. Aisle 7 comes _____ aisle 12.

14. June 29 comes _____ June 30.

15. Exit 15 comes _____ exit 22.

Missing Bone

McAllister the Mutt is dog-tired from walking in circles trying to find his bone. To help him find the path to the bone, move one paw print at a time in any direction except diagonally. You can only follow the tracks that have odd numbers. Draw a line to show his route.

Patterns for the Mail Carrier

Meimei the mail carrier is delivering letters. Give her some help. Fill in the missing addresses on the houses below.

Extra

What pattern do you see in the house numbers? _____

_____

_____

_____

Presidents' Day Problem

The first 18 Presidents of the United States are listed below.
They are shown in order.

1. George Washington (1789–1797)

2. John Adams (1797–1801)

3. Thomas Jefferson (1801–1809)

4. James Madison (1809–1817)

5. James Monroe (1817–1825)

6. John Quincy Adams (1825–1829)

7. Andrew Jackson (1829–1837)

8. Martin Van Buren (1837–1841)

9. William Henry Harrison (1841)

10. John Tyler (1841–1845)

11. James Knox Polk (1845–1849)

12. Zachary Taylor (1849–1850)

13. Millard Fillmore (1850–1853)

14. Franklin Pierce (1853–1857)

15. James Buchanan (1857–1861)

16. Abraham Lincoln (1861–1865)

17. Andrew Johnson (1865–1869)

18. Ulysses S. Grant (1869–1877)

1. **Which President was Washington?** _____ the 1st _____

2. **Which President was Lincoln?** _____

3. **Which President came before Lincoln?** _____

4. **Which President came after Lincoln?** _____

5. **How many Presidents were there**

   between Washington and Lincoln? _____

Amused Chooser

Compare numbers.

> means greater than   < means less than   = means same as

Hint: The arrow points to the number that is less

Write >, <, or =
in the circles.

1. 11 ◯ 21

2. 56 ◯ 72

3. 47 ◯ 47

4. 64 ◯ 10

5. 59 ◯ 59

6. 38 ◯ 17

7. 526 ◯ 527

8. 159 ◯ 42

Fill in the blanks
with numbers.

9. ____ < ____

10. ____ < ____

11. ____ > ____

12. ____ < ____

13. ____ = ____

14. ____ < ____

15. ____ = ____

16. ____ = ____

Write the
numbers from
greatest to least.

17. 37 54 61 73 _____

18. 22 96 43 24 _____

19. 79 78 69 51 _____

20. 15 27 51 37 _____

Riddle Fun

What wears shoes, sandals, and boots, but has no feet?

A __ __ __ __ __ __ __ __

To find out, write each number in standard form. Then look for the numbers in the puzzle and circle them. They are written up, down, and backward. When you have circled all the numbers given, the letters in the blocks left uncircled spell the answer to the riddle. The first number has been circled for you.

4 B	3 A	2 R	1 K	9 S	9 I	5 G
8 R	1 M	7 Y	1 S	7 O	5 D	6 T
8 D	5 W	1 E	8 T	9 E	1 S	4 S
1 W	6 P	2 C	5 X	3 A	3 Z	9 P
4 L	9 J	7 F	7 S	0 R	7 M	0 L
8 H	3 F	6 Y	9 K	2 T	0 E	9 Q

8 ones 1 ten = **518** 5 hundreds	5 ones 1 ten = 3 hundreds	6 ones 7 tens = 2 hundreds	3 ones 9 tens = 6 hundreds
7 ones 3 tens = 1 hundred	4 ones 6 tens = 5 hundreds	9 ones 0 tens = 9 hundreds	1 one 1 ten = 8 hundreds
9 ones 0 tens = 2 hundreds	7 ones 1 ten = 7 hundreds	6 ones 3 tens = 8 hundreds	1 one 2 tens = 3 hundreds
8 ones 8 tens = 4 hundreds	7 ones 5 tens = 8 hundreds	2 ones 3 tens = 4 hundreds	7 ones 0 tens = 7 hundreds

Pattern Learner

A pattern is a repeated arrangement of numbers, shapes, or lines in a row. Continue the patterns below.

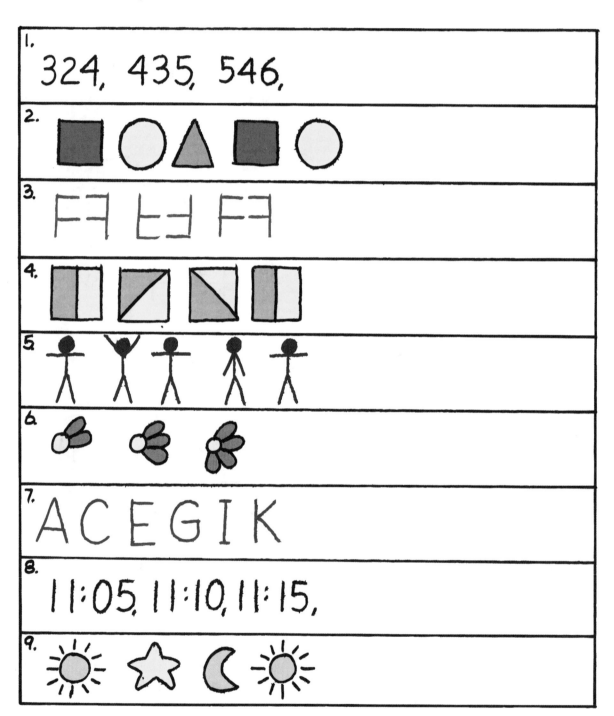

Shape Tricks

Danny's class was learning about shapes. He noticed that you could draw a line across one shape to make two shapes. Draw a line through each shape below to make two new shapes. (Pattern blocks may help you.)

1. Make a square and a triangle.

2. Make two triangles.

3. Make two rectangles.

4. Make a triangle and a diamond.

5. Cut this twice to make 3 triangles.

Picking Out Patterns

On the 100th day of school, everyone in Pat's class picked out patterns on the 100 Chart. Look at the chart below.

1	2	3	4	5	6	7	8	9	10
11	12	13	14	15	16	17	18	19	20
21	22	23	24	25	26	27	28	29	30
31	32	33	34	35	36	37	38	39	40
41	42	43	44	45	46	47	48	49	50
51	52	53	54	55	56	57	58	59	60
61	62	63	64	65	66	67	68	69	70
71	72	73	74	75	76	77	78	79	80
81	82	83	84	85	86	87	88	89	90
91	92	93	94	95	96	97	98	99	100

Find and finish the pattern starting with 2, 12, 22

_____

Find and finish the pattern starting with 100, 90, 80

_____

Find and finish the pattern starting with 97, 87, 77

_____

Find and finish the pattern starting with 11, 22, 33

_____

Shape Study

A heptagon has 7 sides. On a heptagon, all the sides are the same length.

Connect the dots in the geoboards below to make other shapes with 7 sides.

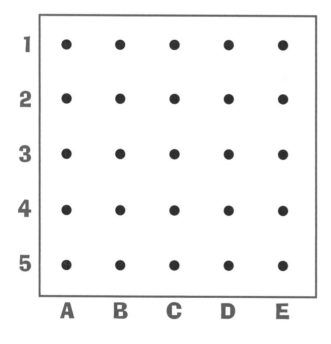

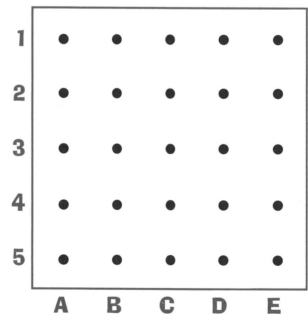

Shape Gaper

FLAT SHAPES HAVE LENGTH AND WIDTH.

A
SQUARE

B
CIRCLE

C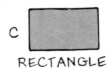
RECTANGLE

D
TRIANGLE

SOLID SHADES HAVE LENGTH AND WIDTH AND DEPTH.

E
CUBE

F
SPHERE

G
CYLINDER

H
CONE

I
RECTANGULAR PRISM

J
PYRAMID

MATCH THE SHAPES WITH THESE OBJECTS. USE THE LETTERS ABOVE.

A.

1.	BALL
2.	WASTEBASKET
3.	RING
4.	POSTAGE STAMP
5.	BIRDHOUSE
6.	CRAYON BOX
7.	ICE CUBE
8.	APOLLO SPACECRAFT
9.	TRASH BARREL
10.	JAR
11.	ENVELOPE

B.

1.	COMPACT DISC
2.	AN ORANGE
3.	A PENNANT
4.	A BUILDING
5.	FISH BOWL
6.	CHILD'S BLOCK
7.	CHECKERS (GAME)
8.	A SAIL ON A SMALL BOAT
9.	CEREAL BOX
10.	PLANET EARTH
11	STICK OF BUTTER

C.

1.	ROAD MARKER
2.	FLAG
3.	SHEET OF PAPER
4.	FLASHLIGHT
5.	SOUP CAN
6.	POSTER
7.	BASEBALL
8.	TRAIN CAR
9.	A DIME
10.	PHOTOGRAPH
11.	WORLD GLOBE

Rocket Riddle

What did the rocket say when it left the party?

What To Do

To find the answer to the riddle, solve the multiplication problems. Then match each product with a letter in the Key below. Write the correct letters on the blanks below.

1　5 x 1 = _____　　**6**　5 x 2 = _____

2　8 x 1 = _____　　**7**　6 x 2 = _____

3　11 x 1 = _____　　**8**　8 x 2 = _____

4　26 x 1 = _____　　**9**　9 x 2 = _____

5　3 x 2 = _____　　**10**　12 x 2 = _____

Key

10	F	27	U	20	W
13	C	8	E	7	D
11	O	6	K	12	T
16	E	9	B	26	O
5	A	24	F	18	T

Riddle Answer: "TIM ___ ___ ___ ___ ___ ___ ___ ___ ___ ___."

 8 **7** **3** **9** **1** **5** **2** **4** **6** **10**

Wise Owls

What did the owl say when someone knocked on its door?

What To Do

To find the answer to the riddle, solve the multiplication problems. Then match each product with a letter in the Key below. Write the correct letters on the blanks below.

1 5 x 3 = _____

2 2 x 3 = _____

3 8 x 3 = _____

4 4 x 3 = _____

5 9 x 3 = _____

6 6 x 3 = _____

7 10 x 3 = _____

8 12 x 3 = _____

9 11 x 3 = _____

10 0 x 3 = _____

Key

30	O	8	K	42	N
11	A	15	O	24	T
36	H	0	I	33	O
18	I	27	O	6	Q
32	F	6	S	12	W

Riddle Answer: " ___ ___ ___ ___ ___ ___   ___ ___   ___ ___ ?"

Jack's Beanstalk

Jack's class was growing bean plants.
After 1 week, Jack's was the tallest.
Measure Jack's plant below. Record its height: _____
After 2 weeks, Jack's plant had doubled in height.
How tall was it now? _____

Draw a picture to show how tall the plant grew.
Measure your drawing to make sure it is the correct height.

2 weeks.

After 3 weeks, Jack's plant was still growing!

How tall would it be now? _____

Explain your answer. _____

_____

Candy Boxes

Steve works in a candy store. He puts candy into boxes. Each box has 10 spaces. Steve has 32 candies. Try to draw 32 candies in the boxes below. Write the number of candies in each box on the line. Write the number of any leftover candy at the bottom of the page.

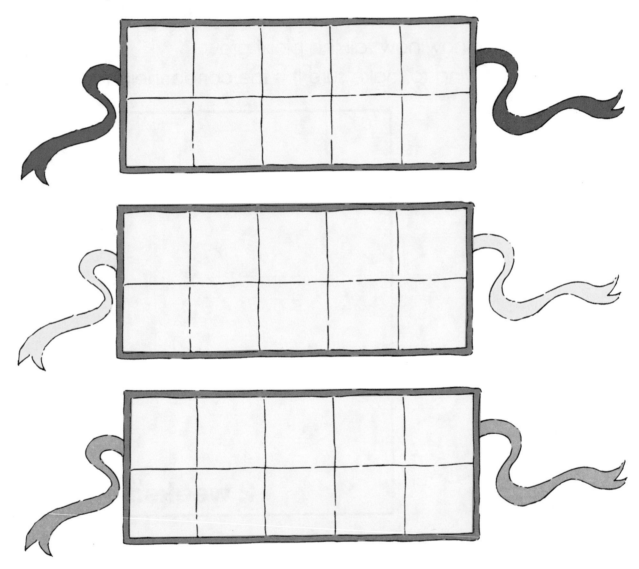

Extra

Leftover candies: _____

Creature Categories

Nick's class took a field trip to the beach. When they looked in the tide pools, they saw a lot of animals. Group the animals they saw. Color the animals in each group the same color.

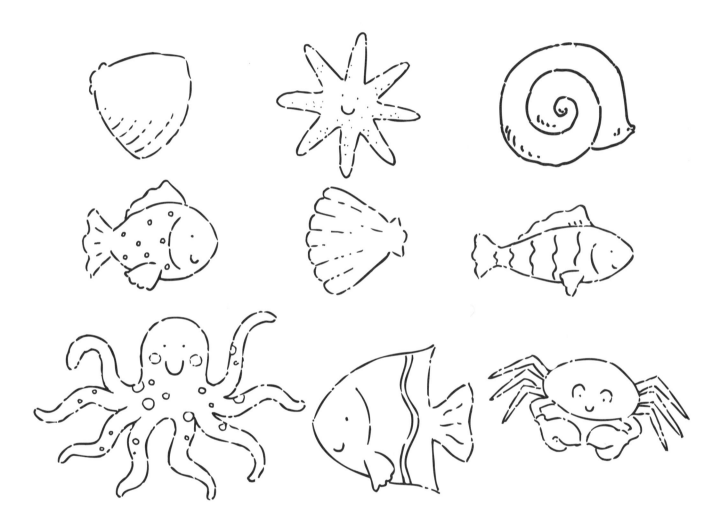

Write a word or phrase that explains how you grouped them.

Group #1 _____

Group #2 _____

Group #3 _____

Coin-Toss Addition

Toss 8 coins. Write "**H**" for heads or "**T**" for tails in the circles below to show your toss. Then write the addition equation. Write the number of "heads" first. We did the first one for you. Try it three times.

(**H**) (**H**) (**H**) (**H**) (**T**) (**T**) (**T**) (**T**)

Equation: _____ $4 + 4 = 8$ _____

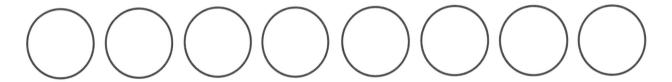

Equation: _____

Equation: _____

Equation: _____

Clear Reader

Write each sentence using numbers and symbols.

1. Four plus five is nine.	
2. Eleven minus six is five.	
3. Nine plus seven is sixteen.	
4. Four plus eight is twelve.	
5. Three minus two is one.	
6. Seven plus seven is fourteen.	
7. Fifteen minus ten is five.	
8. Two plus eight is ten.	
9. Five minus two is three.	

Time to Get Up!

Twenty animals were hibernating near Sleepy Pond.
5 of them woke up. Color 5 animals below.

How many are still sleeping? _____

A week later, 7 more woke up. Color 7 other animals.

How many are still sleeping? _____

Pizza Party

Garth's class is having a pizza party. They made a diagram to show which pizzas they would like. Draw an X in each circle to show how many classmates wanted each kind of pizza.

- 5 wanted cheese pizza.
- 10 wanted pepperoni pizza.
- 3 wanted sausage pizza.
- 2 wanted both cheese and pepperoni pizza.

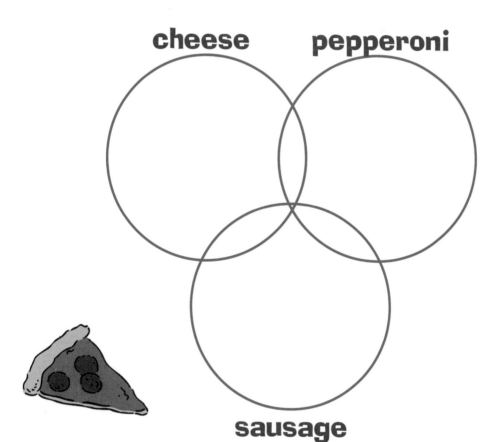

cheese   **pepperoni**

sausage

What can you learn by looking at this diagram? Write your ideas:

_____

_____

Prime Timer

Write the time 2 ways.

Example: 1:15
15 minutes after 1

1

_____ minutes to _____

4

_____ minutes to _____

2

_____ minutes after _____

5

_____ minutes after _____

3

_____ minutes to _____

6

_____ minutes after _____

Money Matters

Alex asked his little brother Billy to trade piggy banks.

Alex's bank has these coins: **Billy's has these coins:**

Do you think this is a fair trade? _____

Test your answer:

Add up Alex's coins: _____

Add up Billy's coins: _____

Write the totals in this Greater Than/Less Than equation:

_____ > _____

Who has more money? _____

Just Snacks

Use the menu on the next page to answer
the following questions.

1. Which snack costs the most?

   _____

   How much do they cost?

   _____

2. Which sweet costs the least? _____

   How much does it cost? _____

3. Henry spends 50¢ on a snack.

   What does he buy? _____

4. Gina orders a drink. She spends 15¢.

   Which drink does she order? _____

5. Dan orders popcorn and a cookie.

   How much does he pay? _____

6. Pat buys a cup of soup and a sip of milk.

   How much does she spend? _____

Small Snacks

Potato Chips	60¢
Pretzels	45¢
Popcorn	55¢
Peanuts	50¢
Bagel Bites	65¢
Teeny Sandwiches	75¢
Cup of Soup	40¢

Small Sweets & Drinks

Cookie	40¢
Donut Hole	25¢
Ice Cream Bar	60¢
Raisins	30¢
Sip of Milk	10¢
Gulp of Juice	15¢

Best Estimator

LENGTH CAN BE MEASURED IN INCHES (IN.), FEET (FT.), YARDS (YD.), AND MILES (MI.). 12 IN. = 1 FT. 5280 FT. = 1 MILE.

UNDERLINE THE MORE SENSIBLE MEASURE.

How many inches to Boston, Sir?

BUS STOP

7. LENGTH OF A FOOTBALL FIELD
   INCHES   YARDS

8. DISTANCE FROM EARTH TO MOON
   MILES   YARDS

9. DEPTH OF A SWIMMING POOL
   FEET   INCHES

1. HEIGHT OF A BOOKCASE
   INCHES   FEET

10. TUBE OF TOOTHPASTE
    INCHES   FEET

2. WIDTH OF YOUR BACKYARD
   YARDS   MILES

11. HEIGHT OF A REFRIGERATOR
    INCHES   FEET

3. LENGTH OF A RIVER
   MILES   YARDS

12. WIDTH OF A BEDROOM
    FEET   INCHES

4. WIDTH OF A DESK
   INCHES   FEET

13. DISTANCE BETWEEN 2 CITIES
    YARDS   MILES

5. LENGTH OF YOUR ARM
   FEET   INCHES

14. LENGTH OF A DOLLAR
    INCHES   FEET

6. LENGTH OF A COMB
   INCHES   FEET

15. LENGTH OF AN AUTOMOBILE
    INCHES   FEET

December Weather

In December, Mrs. Monroe's class drew the weather on a calendar. Each kind of weather has a picture:

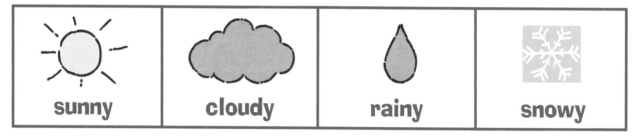

| sunny | cloudy | rainy | snowy |

Look at the calendar. Answer the questions below.

How many sunny days did they have? _____

How many cloudy days did they have? _____

How many rainy days did they have? _____

How many snowy days did they have? _____

Which kind of weather did they have the most? _____

Measuring Perimeter

Use the inch side of a ruler and measure each side of each triangle. Write the inches in the spaces below. Then add up all the sides to find the perimeter, or distance around each triangle.

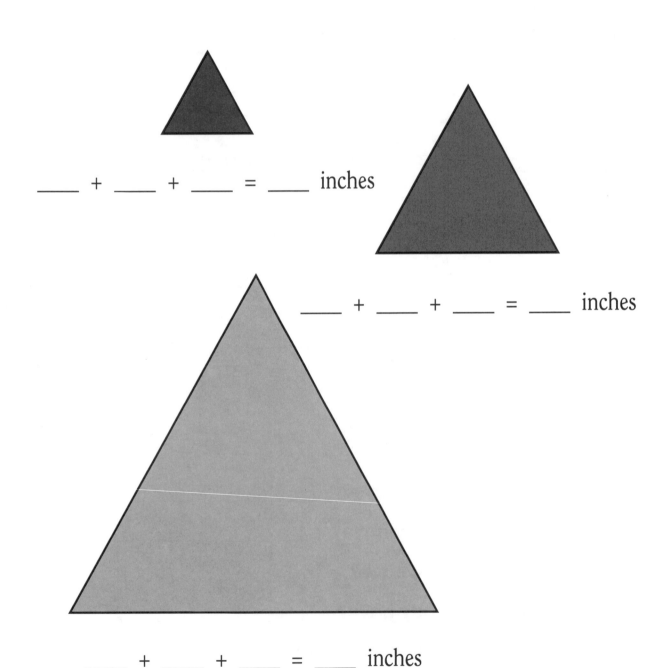

___ + ___ + ___ = ___ inches

___ + ___ + ___ = ___ inches

___ + ___ + ___ = ___ inches

Night-Light

1. Find each number pair on the graph. Make a dot for each.
2. Connect the dots in the order that you make them.
3. What picture did you make?

_____

	Across	Up
1.	6	11
2.	5	7
3.	1	7
4.	4	5
5.	3	0
6.	6	3
7.	9	0
8.	8	5
9.	11	7
10.	7	7
11.	6	11

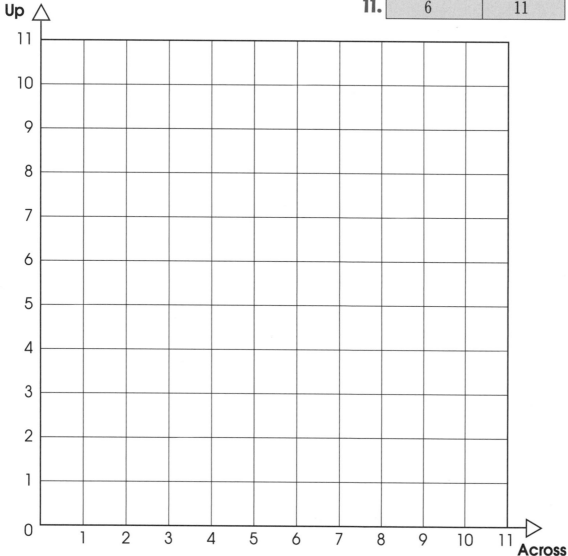

Great Graphing

The picture was made with 7 different shapes. How many of each shape was used? Color in the shapes, following the instructions. Then color in the boxes on the chart, 1 box for each shape used.

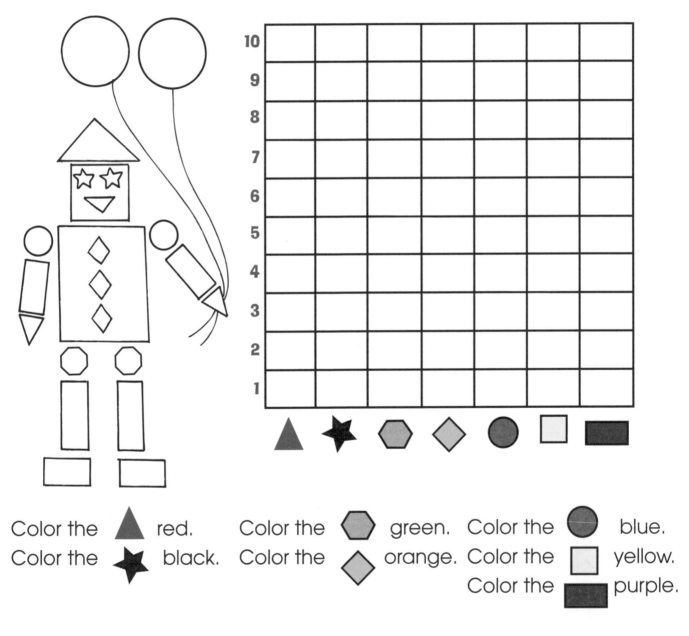

Color the ▲ red.   Color the ⬡ green.   Color the ● blue.
Color the ★ black.   Color the ◆ orange.   Color the ▢ yellow.
                                             Color the ▬ purple.

© Scholastic Inc.

Which shape was used the most? _____

Fruit Graph

Ask 12 friends which of these four fruits they like most. Fill in the graph to find out. Color one box on the graph for each vote.

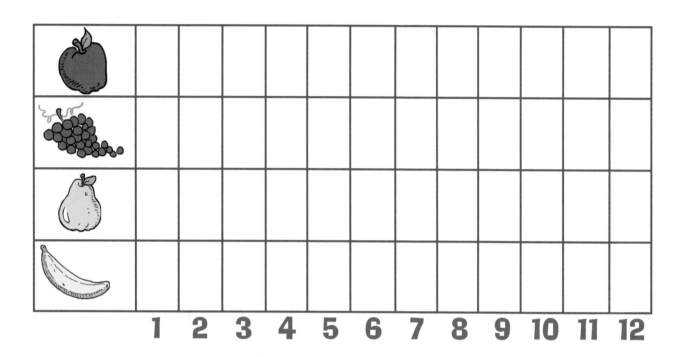

Which fruit was the most popular? _____

How many votes did it get? _____

Which fruit was the least popular? _____

How many votes did it get? _____

If two fruits got the same amount of votes, they "tied."

Write any ties below.

_____ **and** _____

_____ **and** _____

Chester's Cakes and Pies

Fill in the blanks. Chester Chipmunk was cutting cakes and pies.
Bobby Bear said, "Some aren't cut in half. When you cut something in half, there are _____ pieces and both of the pieces are the same _____."

Here is how Chester cut the cakes and pies.

Circle the desserts that are cut in half correctly.

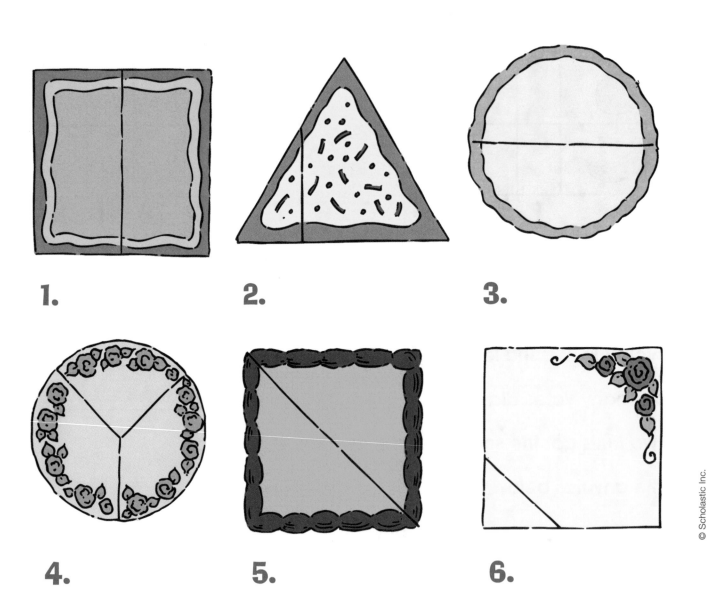

1. **2.** **3.**

4. **5.** **6.**

Part Timer

Determine fractions of a whole. Check √ your answers.

1. HOW MUCH
JUICE IS LEFT?

$\frac{1}{2}$
$\frac{1}{4}$
$\frac{1}{3}$

2. HOW MUCH
PIZZA IS GONE?

$\frac{1}{2}$
$\frac{1}{3}$
$\frac{1}{8}$

3. HOW MUCH
HAS BEEN EATEN?

$\frac{1}{3}$
$\frac{1}{6}$
$\frac{1}{4}$

4. HOW MUCH
IS GONE?

$\frac{1}{4}$
$\frac{1}{2}$
$\frac{1}{8}$

5. HOW MUCH
IS LACED?

$\frac{1}{2}$
$\frac{1}{3}$
$\frac{1}{4}$

6. HOW MUCH
TONIC IS LEFT?

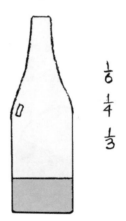

$\frac{1}{6}$
$\frac{1}{4}$
$\frac{1}{3}$

7. HOW MUCH
WATER IS LEFT?

$\frac{3}{4}$
$\frac{1}{2}$
$\frac{1}{4}$

8. HOW MUCH
HAS BEEN CUT OFF?

$\frac{1}{2}$ $\frac{1}{4}$
$\frac{1}{3}$

9. HOW MUCH WATER REMAINS?

$\frac{3}{4}$ $\frac{1}{2}$ $\frac{1}{4}$

10. HOW MUCH LEAF
HAS BEEN EATEN?

$\frac{1}{4}$
$\frac{1}{6}$
$\frac{2}{3}$

11. HOW MUCH BREAD IS UNCUT?

$\frac{1}{4}$ $\frac{1}{3}$ $\frac{1}{2}$

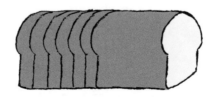

Fraction Fun

Something that is split in 2 equal parts is divided in "half."

These two shapes are divided in half.

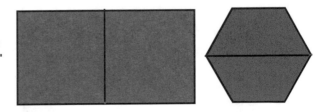

> **A fraction has a number on the top:** ⟶ 1
>
> **A fraction has a number on the bottom, too:** ⟶ 2
>
> **The top number tells the "fraction," or parts, of the whole.**
>
> **The bottom number tells the number of parts in the whole.**

Draw a line to match the picture with a fraction.

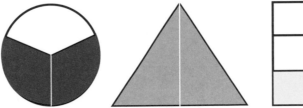

$$\frac{2}{2} \qquad \frac{2}{12} \qquad \frac{2}{3}$$

The top number in these fractions tells you how many parts to color. Try it!

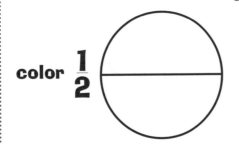

color $\dfrac{1}{2}$

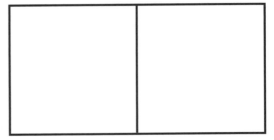

color $\dfrac{2}{2}$

Fun With Fractions

A fraction has two numbers. The top number will tell you how many parts to color. The bottom number tells you how many parts there are.

Color 1/5 of the circle.

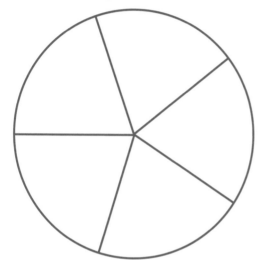

Color 4/5 of the rectangle.

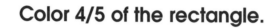

Color 3/5 of the ants.

Color 2/5 of the spiders.

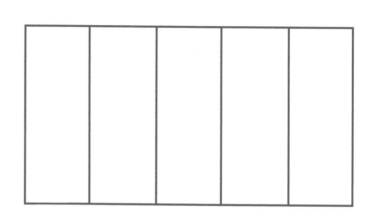

Color 0/5 of the bees.

Color 5/5 of the worms.

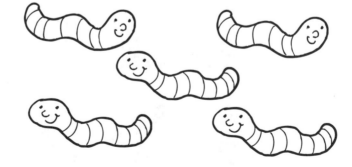

More Fun With Fractions

A fraction has two numbers. The top number will tell you how many parts to color. The bottom number tells you how many total parts there are.

$\frac{10}{10}$ is the whole circle.

$\frac{10}{10}$ is the whole rectangle.

Color $\frac{8}{10}$ of the circle.

Color $\frac{4}{10}$ of the rectangle.

How much is not colored? ____

How much is not colored? ____

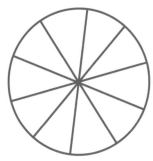

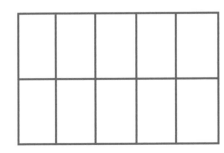

$\frac{10}{10} - \frac{8}{10} = \underline{\quad}$

$\frac{10}{10} - \frac{4}{10} = \underline{\quad}$

Solve this fraction equation. Cross out the dogs to help you.

$\frac{10}{10} - \frac{3}{10} = \underline{\quad}$

Answer Key

READING COMPREHENSION

Page 12
1. spots; My domino has two white spots, and yours has five. 2. sea bird; A gray seabird flew by the cruise ship. 3. A green stone; The queen had a beautiful necklace made of a green stone. 4. flute player; My sister is the best flute player in the high school band.

Page 13
Neil Armstrong was the first man to walk on the moon.

Page 14
1. IOU; 2. EZ; 3. ICU; 4. AB; 5. TP; 6. MT; 7. IV

Page 15
Police officers help people.

Page 16
On Saturday, Rachel got up early. Mom was still asleep, so Rachel made her own breakfast. She put some peanut butter in a bowl. She mixed it with a little *honey. Then she stirred in some *oatmeal, *bran flakes, and *raisins. It tasted yummy! When Mom got up, she said, "Oh, You made granola!"

B	R	A	N	F	L	A	K	E	S	M	H	N	C	L
O	A	T	M	E	A	L	B	K	E	Q	O	J	W	I
W	R	A	I	S	I	N	S	G	R	A	N	O	L	A
L	G	S	A	T	U	R	D	A	Y	P	E	R	D	R
G	R	A	C	H	E	L	Y	U	M	M	Y	F	A	H

Page 17
1. B; 2. U; 3. L; 4. L; 5. R ; 6. I; 7. D; 8. E; 9. R; 10. S; Bullriders

Page 18

```
  N A P
  F
F R U I T
  I
W I C
G O R I L L A S
R                L
E   C H E S T S  E
S   L            E
T   L            P
L
V I N E S
```

Page 19
Make-believe: pig, goat and sheep, horses, pizza and hamburgers, mouse and table, golden eggs, crickets (The others are real.)

Page 20
Real: a woman feeding animals; a grandmother living alone; sleeping on hay in a barn; a house burning down; crying that her house burned (The rest are make-believe.)

Page 21
Answers will vary.

Page 22
1. Mia begged Spooky to come down. 2. Mia asked Mr. Carson for help. 3. Mr. Carson called his firefighter friends. 4. The fire truck came. 5. A firefighter climbed the ladder. 6. Spooky jumped to a tree and climbed down. 7. Mia scolded Spooky. 8. The firefighters laughed.

Page 23
Writing; Math; Recess; Social Studies; 11:00; Story Time; Science; Spelling; Music

Page 24
3, 1, 4, 2, 6, 7, 5, 8

Page 25
(Your child's name) knows how to follow directions!

Page 26
Check your child's picture.

Page 27
1. 50; 2. (your state); 4. 13; 6. Old Glory; 7. allegiance, America, Republic, indivisible, liberty, justice

Page 28
1. math; 2. taking out the trash; 3. playing a video game; 4. going to bed

Page 29
1. Backward Day
2. Check your child's dot-to-dot picture.
3. 50, 45, 40, 35, 30, 25, 20, 15, 10, 5

Page 30
1. stealing; paid for it; 2. showed bad manners; said "Excuse me"; 3. lying; told the truth; 4. hurt his feelings; helped him

Page 31
Each tree should be illustrated as described in the story.

Page 32
1. box shape; 2. heart shape; 3. circle shape; 4. semi-circle shape; 5. arc shape

Page 33

1. Zolak's shadow; 2. No; 3. No; He didn't see a real earthling, only his own shadow.
4.

Page 34

1, 4, 6, 7, 10, 11, 14, 15, 18, 20, 21, 24, 26, teapot

Page 35

People Who Went to the Beach: Dad, Mom, Tim, and Tara
What They Did: swam, fished, built sandcastles, went sailing
Picnic Items: ham sandwiches, potato chips, apples, cookies, lemonade
Living Things They Saw on the Beach: crab, dog, starfish, sea gulls

Page 36

1. ~~cheerful~~; angry; 2. ~~away~~; west; 3. ~~goat~~; parakeet; 4. ~~mud~~; lemonade; 5. ~~toy~~; arm; 6. ~~Sarah~~; George; 7. ~~spinach~~; pudding; 8. ~~bicycle~~; crayon; 9. ~~marble~~; dime
Birds 3; Desserts 7; Bad Feelings 1; Boys' Names 6; Money 9; School Supplies 8; Directions 2; Body Parts 5; Drinks 4

Page 37

Answers will vary.

Page 38

1. He learned to fly. 2. All of a sudden something wonderful happened! 3. afraid; 4. proud

Page 39

(Accept any reasonable answers.)
1. The home team wins the game.
2. The brownies will burn. 3. She will have a flat tire. 4. It will rain.
5. Mom will fall. 6. The boat will sink.

Page 40

Your child should draw pictures that show these conclusions: Rita became a rabbit again. Diana became a duck again.

Page 41

Ryan—giant tortoise, three-toed sloth
Both—albino alligator
Jessica—giraffe, owl

Page 42

Both had twenty dollars to spend. Joey bought sweets. Harry bought breakfast food.

Page 43

both, Kendra, Lacey, Lacey, both, Lacey, Lacey, Kendra, Lacey, Kendra, Lacey

Page 44

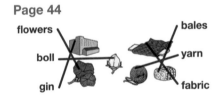

Things made of cotton: shirt, pillow, sock, shorts, towel
Things not made of cotton: scissors, pitcher, trumpet, cake

Page 45

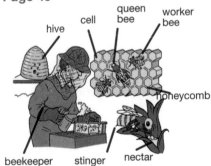

Page 46

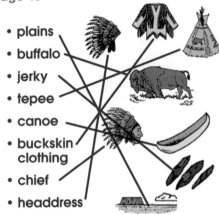

- plains
- buffalo
- jerky
- tepee
- canoe
- buckskin clothing
- chief
- headdress

Your child should put an X on the pictures of the computer, the helicopter, and the car. Other pictures should be circled.

Page 47

The girls got too loud, so Dad said to be quiet. The girls saw a bee land on Dad's bald head, so Mary Beth whopped Dad on the head with a book. The car ran off the road and through a fence, which let the cows out.

Page 48

1. spewing hot ash into the air;
2. for people and animals to breathe;
3. flattened trees; 4. forest fires;
5. floods and mudslides; 6. it still erupts from time to time

Page 49

1. Dr. Smileyface makes his patients laugh.
2. The child who wrote this story is not afraid to go to the dentist.
3. Dr. Smileyface teaches kids how to take care of their teeth.
4. Dr. Smileyface sends kids home with a surprise.

Page 50

HELPING OTHERS

Page 51
1. ~~Man~~; Lady; 2. ~~hot dogs~~; chicken nuggets; 3. ~~frowns~~; smiles; 4. ~~Miss Daniels~~; Lunch Lady; 5. ~~hardware~~; shoe; 6. ~~mean~~; kind

Page 52
Your child should circle Jed, bed, and head. They should draw a green box around long and wrong. Daisy, lazy, class, pass, crazy

Page 53
Paul Bunyan was a mighty man. He was so big, he had to use wagon wheels for buttons. Paul was a lumberjack. He owned a blue ox named Babe. Paul and Babe were so big that their tracks made 10,000 lakes in the state of Minnesota.

Paul worked with seven axmen. They were so big that they were six feet tall sitting down. All of them were named Elmer. So when Paul called "Elmer!" they all came running.

The year of the two winters, it got so cold that when the axmen would speak, their words froze in midair. When it thawed in the spring, there was a terrible chatter for weeks.

One time Paul caught two giant mosquitoes and used them to drill holes in maple trees.

Paul Bunyan had a purple cow named Lucy. In the year of two winters, it got so cold that Lucy's milk turned to ice cream before it hit the pail.

Page 54
Check your child's work to be sure he or she has correctly identified stage directions.

GRAMMAR

Page 102
1. T   2. Q   3. Q   4. T   5. T
6. Q   7. T

Page 103
1. The vet is nice.
2. She helped my dog.
3. Did she see your cat?
4. Is the cat well now?
5. My cat feels better.
6. Will he take the cat home?

Page 104
1. correct as is   2. The vet
3. cats.   4. correct as is   5. Do you
6. When is   7. He has   8. the vet.
9. goldfish?   10. Will you

Page 105
1. E   2. C   3. E   4. E   5. E
6. C   7. Be yourself!
8. Don't copy other people.

Page 106
1. fear   2. excitement   3. surprise
4. anger   5. Please don't be upset!
6. Answers will vary.
7. Answers will vary.

Page 107
1. You are a great hopper!
2. The picture looks beautiful!
3. I can paint, too!
4. correct as is
5. Teach me how to hop.
6. Hop backward like this.

Page 108
1. I, .   2. M, I, ?   3. I, !   4. C, I, ?
5. B, I, .
Telling Sentences: I sail my boat in the lake. Bill and I fly the kite.
Questions: May I have a turn? Can Kiku and I play?
Exclamations: I am so happy!

Page 109
1. T   2. C   3. T   4. C   5. Q
6. E   7. Q   8. I, Answers will vary.
9. I, Answers will vary.
10. I, Answers will vary.

Page 110
1. I have fun with my bike.
2. Can I ride to the beach?
3. I find a pretty shell.
4. correct as is
5. Get the shovel.
6. What a mess I made!

Page 111
1. boy, boat   2. brothers, park
3. girl, grandmother   4. boats, lake
5. Friends, needle, thread, sail
People: boy, brothers, girl, grandmother, friends
Places: park, lake
Things: boat, boats, needle, thread, sail

Page 112
Circled nouns: village, office, cane, pencil, doctor, boy, bed, aunt, school
People: doctor, boy, aunt
Places: village, school, office
Things: cane, pencil, bed

Page 113
1. swing   2. bench   3. children
4. carousel   5. bridge   6. stream

Page 114
1. no   2. yes   3. no   4. yes
5. place   6. person   7. person
8. thing

Page 115
1. George Ancona   2. Mexico
3. Jorgito   4. Coney Island
5. Honduras   6. Tío Mario
People: George Ancona, Jorgito, Tío Mario
Places: Mexico, Coney Island, Honduras.

Page 116
1. Sue   2. California
3. Los Angeles   4. Pacific Ocean
5. Tonya   6. Sue Wong
7. Shore Road   8. Austin, Texas
Answers will vary.

Page 117
1. person 2. place 3. person
4. place 5. Emilio 6. Orlando
7. Disney World 8. Main Street

Page 118
1. runs 2. wears 3. smacks
4. holds 5. misses 6. waits
7. writes 8. helps

Page 119
1. watch 2. throws 3. opens
4. cheers 5. hits 6. runs
7. yells 8. eat

Page 120
1. action verb 2. not an action verb
3. not an action verb 4. not an action
verb 5. action verb
6. action verb 7. not an action verb
8. action verb 9. action verb
10. not an action verb

Page 121
The following get an X next to them.
2. (Crow) could not get a drink.
3. (The water) rose.
6. (One mouse) had a plan.

Page 122
1. a. Lin likes to play soccer.
2. b. Her friends watch her play.
3. a. They cheer for Lin.
4. a. Her mom goes to all of her
    games.
5. a. The coach is very proud of Lin.

Page 123
1. telling part 2. naming part
3. not the whole part 4. not the
whole part 5. saw the cat go away
6. Then the bird 7. After a minute,
the cat 8. walked back, too

Page 124
1. planted 2. watered 3. weeded
4. discovered 5. (blank) 6. pulled

Page 125
1. pushed 2. splashed 3. rolled
4. followed 5. washed
Answers will vary.

Page 126
1. visited 2. correct as is
3. correct as is 4. talked 5. asked
6. correct as is 7. correct as is
8. showed

Page 127
1. He, Wendell 2. She, Mother
3. They, The pigs 4. it, a board
game 5. They, The pigs and
Wendell 6. He, Wendell

Page 128
1. it 2. They 3. It 4. she 5. He

Page 129
1. Mrs. Fultz 2. The boy
3. The house 4. The pigs
5. He 6. they

Page 130
Exclamation: What a big mango! This
tastes great!
Command: Buy me an avocado.
Come over for dinner.
Question: Is that a banana?
Did you find the fruit?
Telling Sentence: I want to eat
dinner. I like mangoes.

Page 131
1. . T 2. ? Q 3. . T 4. . C
5. ! E 6. . C 7. ? Q 8. ! E

Page 132
1. command 2. question
3. exclamation 4. command
5. exclamation 6. telling
7. question 8. telling

Page 133
1. Two brothers can live together.
2. Hungbu will find a new home.
3. Mother will fix the house.
4. Will you clean the house?
5. Can the bird help them?

Page 134
1. Will I find some wood? QUESTION
2. Each of us must help.
   STATEMENT
3. Where are the trees?
   QUESTION
4. That is your pumpkin.
   Is that your pumpkin?
5. You can help cut the pumpkin.
   Can you help cut the pumpkin?

Page 135
1. Dad made eggs for breakfast.
2. He cracked open four eggs.
3. Do you like eggs?
4. Did you help him?
5. Beat eggs with a fork.
6. correct as is

Page 136
1. accordion(s) 2. brush(es)
3. clock(s), watch(es) 4. flower(s),
box(es); accordions, clocks, flowers
brushes, watches, boxes

Page 137
1. sandwiches 2. lunches
3. lunchboxes 4. dishes 5. boxes
6. dresses 7. coats 8. benches

Page 138
1. sketches 2. correct as is
3. foxes 4. correct as is
5. correct as is 6. dresses
7. balls 8. correct as is

Page 139
1. brown donkey, heavy sack
2. striped cat, two birds
3. little rooster, six times
4. brown, heavy, striped, little
5. two, six

Page 140
1. zoo, big 2. giraffe, tall
3. girls, two 4. spots, brown
color word: brown
size words: tall, big
number word: two

Page 141
1. red   2. yellow   3. purple   4. big
5. three   6. little   7. huge   8. Two

Page 142
1. is, now   2. are, now   3. were, past   4. is, now   5. am, now
6. was, past

Page 143
1. is/was, one   2. is/was, one
3. were, more   4. are, more
5. was, one   6. are, more

Page 144
1. past, one
2. present, more than one
3. past, more than one
4. past, more than one
5. past, more than one
6. present, one

Page 145
1. present   2. present   3. present
4. present   5. past   6. past
7. past   8. past

Page 146
1. went   2. goes   3. does   4. did
5. Do   6. go

Page 147
1. goes   2. do   3. does   4. go
5. did   6. went   7. went   8. did

Page 148
1. "Let's go on a picnic."
2. "That's a great idea."
3. "What should we bring?"
4. "We should bring food."
5. "Yes, let's bring lots and lots of food."
6. "You're no help at all!"
7. Answers will vary.

Page 149
1. "It is raining!"
2. "What will we do today?"
3. "We could read."
4. "Maybe the sun will come out soon."
5. "But what will we do now?"
6. "Use your imagination!"
Answers will vary.

Page 150
1. "Let's make a sand castle," said Lenny.
2. "Where's the pail and shovel?" asked Sonya.
3. Sara said, "Maybe Otis can help."
4. "Do you want to dig?" asked Lenny.
5. Sonya shouted, "Get some water!"
6. "Look what we made!" cried the children.

Page 151
1. aren't, are not
2. doesn't, does not
3. can't, cannot
4. couldn't, could not
5. didn't, did not
6. isn't, is not
7. hadn't, had not
8. don't, do not
9. weren't, were not

Page 152
1. couldn't   2. wasn't   3. aren't
4. can't   5. don't   6. didn't
Sentences will vary.

Page 153
1. aren't   2. isn't   3. can't
4. haven't   5. don't   6. didn't
7. couldn't   8. weren't

Page 154
1. writes   2. meets   3. ride
4. shop   5. closes   6. forget
7. locks   8. bang   9. call   10. hear

Page 155
1. play   2. hides   3. chase
4. calls   5. run   6. stand
7. closes   8. nudges
9. sleeps   10. sleep

Page 156
1. make   2. cuts   3. use   4. glow
5. hang   6. buy   7. picks   8. picks
9. wear   10. sell

Page 157
1. camp   2. likes   3. walks   4. build
5. cook   6. crawl
Sentences will vary.

Page 158
1. plays   2. play   3. runs   4. run
5. dive   6. dives   7. climb
8. climbs   9. throw   10. throw

Page 159
1. brings   2. likes   3. trade
4. eat   5. drink   6. buy   7. asks
8. wants   9. puts   10. find

Page 160
1. had; past   2. had; past
3. has; now   4. has; now
5. has; now   6. have; now
7. have; now   8. had; past

Page 161
1. has   2. have   3. had   4. have
5. has   6. had   7. had   8. have
9. has

Page 162
1. correct as is   2. has   3. had
4. had   5. has   6. have
7. correct as is   8. correct as is

WRITING

Page 164
Many of; Our teacher; The reading; The globe; We study; Our class

Page 165
1. Art class; 2. Today we; 3. First, we; 4. The next; 5. My teacher; 6. Next week

Page 166
1. The blue whale is the largest animal in the world. 2. Even dinosaurs were not as large as the blue whale. 3. Blue whales are not part of the fish family. 4. The blue whale has no teeth. 5. Blue whales eat tiny sea creatures. 6. Blue whales have two blowholes.

Page 167
Sentences will vary.

Page 168
1. Where is the king's castle? 2. Who helped Humpty Dumpty? 3. Why did the cow jump over the moon? 4. Will the frog become a prince? 5. Could the three mice see?

Page 169
Sentences will vary.

Page 170
1. .; 2. ?; 3. ?; 4. .; 5. ?; 6. .; 7. ?; 8. .

Page 171
1. The sun is the closest star to Earth. 2. The sun is not the brightest star. 3. What is the temperature of the sun? 4. The sun is a ball of hot gas. 5. How large is the sun? 6. Will the sun ever burn out?

Page 172
Sentences will vary.

Page 173
capital letter; exclamation point; question mark

Dear Mom and Dad,
   Camp is so cool! Today we went swimming. Do you know what the best part of camp is? I think fishing is my favorite thing to do. Did you feed my hamster? I really miss you.
Love, Dalton
Sentences will vary.

Page 174
1. .; 2. ?; 3. !; 4. ?; 5. .; 6. !; 7. ?; 8. .; 9. ?; 10. !; 11. .; 12. ?

Page 175
sentence; question; statement
Sentences will vary.

Page 176
Lists will vary.

Page 177
Lists and sentences will vary.

Page 178
Sentences may vary. Possible answers: 1. A boy climbs a tree in his backyard. 2. A cat plays with fish in the living room. 3. A bunny eats a carrot in the garden.

Page 179
Sentences and pictures will vary.

Page 180
Lists of words will vary.

Page 181
1. fluffy; 2. hard; 3. fuzzy; 4. thin; 5. soft

C	T	R	O	U	G	H
S	H	I	N	Y	B	H
M	S	J	O	W	U	V
O	S	H	Y	B	M	L
O	W	J	Q	B	P	I
T	H	I	C	K	Y	A
H	S	T	I	C	K	Y

Page 182
Answers will vary. Possible answers:
1. fat, three; 2. wooden, cold; 3. Orange, sunny; 4. lazy, muddy; 5. thirsty, shallow; 6. funny, black

Page 183
Describing words will vary.

Page 184
Sentences will vary.

Page 185
Sentences will vary.

Page 186
Sentences will vary.

Page 187
1. The party was fun and exciting. 2. We blew up orange and red balloons. 3. We ate cake and ice cream. 4. The cake frosting was green and yellow. 5. We made a bookmark and a clay pot. 6. We brought games and prizes.

Page 188
1. These peanuts and pretzels are salty.
2. The first graders and second graders eat lunch at noon.
3. Where is the salt and pepper?
4. The napkins and forks are on the table.
5. Are the muffins and cookies in the oven?
6. Michael and Stephen bought lunch today.

Page 189
1. Fill a cup with water and add some flower seeds. 2. This will soften the seeds because they are hard. 3. Fill a cup with dirt while the seeds soak in water. 4. Bury the seeds in the cup until the dirt covers them. 5. Add water to the plant but do not add too much. 6. Set the cup in the sun so the plant will grow.

© Scholastic Inc.

Page 190
Sentences will vary.

Page 191
Sentences will vary.

Page 192
Sentences will vary.

Page 193
Describing words will vary.
1. Sometimes I can see Mars, Jupiter, and Saturn with my telescope.
2. There are many stars in our galaxy.
3. Comets are large pieces of ice and rock.
4. The sun is really a huge star.
5. Is there life on any other planet?
6. Look at that beautiful shooting star!
7. Can you imagine traveling in space?
8. I think I saw a little alien.

Page 194
Describing words will vary.
Saturn is famous for the rings that surround it. Its rings are made of ice, rock, and dirt. The rings circle around the planet. Saturn is made mostly of gas. Saturn's gases are lighter than water. That means Saturn would float if you put it into a tub of water. Saturn has more than 60 moons.

Page 195
1. took; 2. was; 3. saw; 4. many; 5. brought; 6. seen; 7. has; 8. are; 9. were; 10. saw; 11. wore; 12. going; 13. Does; 14. brought

Page 196
1. ~~brang~~, brought; 2. ~~seen~~, saw; 3. ~~gots~~, has; 4. ~~taked~~, took; 5. ~~is~~, are; 6. ~~runned~~, ran; 7. ~~got~~, have; 8. ~~was~~, were; 9. ~~saw~~, see; 10. ~~do~~, does; 11. ~~brang~~, brought; 12. ~~does~~, do

Page 197
Sentences will vary.

Page 198
Sentences will vary.

Page 199
Sentences will vary.

Page 200
Stories will vary.

Page 201
Sentences will vary.

Page 202
Sentences will vary.

Page 203
Sentences will vary.

Page 204
Answers will vary.

Page 205
Stories will vary.

Page 206
Stories will vary.

Page 207
Dear Friend,
 my job as the first president of the United States was hard. My friends and I had to make new laws, new money, and new jobs. the capital was in New York when I became president. then it moved to Philadelphia. Is the capital still there? Who is the president today? I would love to see how the U.S. has changed over the past two hundred years!
                Sincerely,
                George Washington

Page 208
Letters will vary.

MAPS

Page 210
1. yes 2. yes 3. yes 4. no
5. Answers will vary.

Page 211
3. They both show a place from above. 4. A photo has more detail.

Page 212
1. round 2. water 3. land where plants and trees grow

Page 213
1. round 2. smaller 3. the names of places

Pages 214–215
1. An X should be drawn on each continent 2. five
3. Africa, Antarctica, Asia, Australia
4. Atlantic, Arctic 5. A map is flat, but a globe is round.

Page 216
1. north 2. south 3. east 4. west

Page 217
1. Antarctica 2. Arctic Ocean
3. Indian Ocean: east; Europe: east and west; North America: west; Australia: east

Page 218
1. garden 2. south 3. west 4. ice skating rink

Page 219
1. east 2. north 3. west 4. south
5. apartment building

Page 220
Answers from left to right:
4, 6, 3, 2, 1, 5

Page 221
1. school 2. Clark Street 3. railroad
4. green 5. south

Pages 222–223
1. monkeys 2. east 3. yes 4. north
5. Circle Road 6. yes 7. no

Page 224
1. yes 2. no 3. no 4. no 5. yes
6. yes

Page 225
1. Jason 2. Buddy 3. Ellen
4. Mom 5. Buddy

Page 226
1. tennis court 2. B4 3. play golf
4. A2, B2, B1, C1

Page 227
1. B2 2. D2 3. A4 4. C4 5. C1
6. D4

Page 228
1. B1 2. a house 3. First Street
4. no 5. A3

Page 229
1. A4 2. Cincinnati 3. Lake Erie
4. C3 5. B5, C5, C4, D4, D3, D2, D1

Pages 230–231
1. Answers will vary. 2. Salem
3. Austin 4. east 5. Idaho
6. Answers will vary.

Page 232
1. star 2. Lincoln 3. South Dakota
4. Wyoming, Colorado
5. Missouri River

Page 233
1. B3 2. Norfolk 3. B4 4. A3, A4,
A5, B5, C5, C6 5. Wyoming

Pages 234–235
1. Mississippi River 2. so people
could travel there by boat 3. C2
4. Louis Armstrong Park 5. Union
Station 6. B3, B4, B5, C3, C4
7. east

Pages 236–237
1. Austin, Texas 2. Texas 3. United
States 4. larger 5. smaller 6. larger
7. south 8. Map 1: Austin, Texas

Pages 238–239
1. A mountain is much higher than
a plain. 2. a valley 3. possible
answers: a bridge, a boat
4. a plain; because the land is flat
5. a mountain; because the land is
steep 6. Answers will vary.

Page 240
1. ocean 2. swim, fish, sail 3. a river
flows, a lake is surrounded by land

Page 241
Your child should write answers
on the map.

Pages 242–243
1. hills 2. green 3. plains, hills,
mountains 4. west 5. Atlantic
Ocean 6. plains 7. Potomac River
8. Answers will vary.

Pages 244–245
1. 93; north 2. 80 3. Las Vegas
4. Arizona, then Utah 5. 80; east
6. 395 7. 395 south to 50 east or 80
east to 93 south

Page 246
1. Answers will vary.
2. Answers will vary. 3. trees

Page 247
1. yes 2. yes 3. no 4. no 5. yes

Page 248
1. border 2. Mexico 3. north
4. Mexico City 5. west 6. Alaska
7. Rio Grande 8. Canada

Page 250
1. park 2. a book 3. south
4. Town hall 5. west 6. east
7. D1 8. First Street, Bell Avenue,
Second Street, Carol Street

Page 251
1. country border 2. Canada
3. Idaho 4. Columbia River
5. Olympia 6. forest products
7. 5

Page 252
1. compass rose 2. map key
3. island 4. landforms
5. continent 6. mountain
Secret Message: Maps Are Fun

SCIENCE

Page 256
1. pteranodon
2. diplodocus
3. megalosaurus
4. iguanodon
5. apatosaurus
6. velociraptor
7. stegosaurus
8. brachiosaurus
9. allosaurus
10. triceratops

Pages 257–261
Investigation 1: Your child should
notice the following: the closer the
flashlight is to the puppet, the larger
the shadow; the shadow becomes
a thin sliver by giving the puppet a
quarter turn; moving the flashlight
will move the shadow.
Investigation 2: Results will vary
depending on the material used.

Pages 262–263
At first glance, hamsters and gerbils look
alike. Both are soft and adorable rodents.
Both make good pets. Can you tell them apart?
One way is to compare how they look.
They can be the same size, but look at their
tails. A hamster tail is short and stubby. A gerbil
tail is as long as the rest of its body. Now notice
their heads. The hamster's head is round with
chubby cheeks. The gerbil's head is narrow, like
a mouse's.
Or you could compare habits. A gerbil
plays all day and sleeps at night. In contrast,
a hamster sleeps during the day. Suppose you
have one of each. If the sound of little feet
running on a wheel wakes you up at night, you
can probably blame your hamster.

1. D; Sample answer: The first paragraph used glance and then look alike.
2. B; Sample answer: It says that gerbils play all day and sleep at night.
3. Sample answer: Hamsters have short tails but gerbils have long ones. And hamsters have round chubby faces but gerbils have narrow faces.
4. Sample answer: Gerbils sleep at night, but hamsters sleep during the day.

Pages 264–265

The giant anteater has a perfect name. It's very big, and it eats ants—thousands of them a day. And it doesn't even have teeth! This animal's head fits its needs. It has a **keen** sense of smell. It sniffs out an anthill with its powerful nose. Then it uses its sharp claws to open a hole in the anthill. Now its long, wormlike tongue gets busy. The anteater pokes its tongue deep into the hole. Ants stick to it. The anteater snaps its tongue back into its mouth. It scrapes the ants off and swallows them whole.

But feeding like this isn't easy. Ants sting the tongue. So the anteater must stop to rest it after a minute or so. It goes back later for more, after its tongue stops hurting.

1. D; Sample answer: Every paragraph gave information about giant anteaters.
2. B; Sample answer: It says that the anteater has a powerful nose. Strong means about the same thing.
3. Sample answer: The name tells exactly what the animal is. It is big and eats ants.
4. Sample answer: The long pointy snout is good for getting into the anthills. The long sticky tongue helps grab ants.

Page 266

turtle, snake, frog, toad, alligator, lizard, crocodile, tortoise
1. tadpoles; 2. amphibians; 3. legs; 4. cold; 5. 100; 6. reptiles

Page 267

head, eyes, antennae, legs, thorax, wings, abdomen, stinger; one million; beetle; Atlas

Page 268

G	R	A	S	S	H	O	P	P	E	R	C
B	W	E	R	L	A	D	Y	B	U	G	R
E	Y	B	U	T	T	E	R	F	L	Y	I
E	U	I	K	M	N	A	N	T	F	F	C
M	O	T	H	L	J	K	U	Y	S	A	K
R	T	E	Q	A	R	O	A	C	H	O	E
B	E	E	T	L	E	Y	S	I	M	P	T
N	F	H	J	M	O	S	Q	U	I	T	O

Pages 269–273

Investigation 1: The sugar cubes will mostly or completely dissolve by 100 drops of water. The remaining clay will be shaped, much in the same way that caves are shaped by water.
Investigation 2: Results will vary. Signs of erosion include soil that has washed out of the container and channels cut into the soil by running water.

Pages 274–275

1. C; Sample answer: Erosion makes rocks change their size and shape by wearing them away and breaking off parts.
2. D; Sample answer: It says that changes from weathering take a long time.
3. Sample answer: Wind blows little bits of dust and pebbles up against big rocks. This rubbing makes bits of the big rock break off.
4. Sample answer: Picture 1 shows a rock cracked by water. It looks like a broken heart. Picture 2 shows rocks weathered by wind. They look lumpy and rough, like they were scraped. Picture 3 shows weathering by waves, which wore away a big hole in the middle (lines 19–23).

Pages 276–277

Thousands of fans fill Candlestick Park in San Francisco. A handful of ballplayers are on the field. They are stretching, chatting, and warming up. The start of Game 3 of the 1989 World Series between the Giants and the Oakland Athletics is moments away. Excitement fills the air.

Suddenly, everything changes. The huge stadium begins to rumble and swing. Lights go out. Cracks form and chunks of concrete fall from the upper deck. **Alarmed** fans head for the exits. What happened?

What happened is that rock beneath the Earth's surface had suddenly moved. Then the ground began to shake. San Francisco was having a major earthquake!

Bridges buckled and buildings swayed. Highways collapsed. The earthquake caused a halt in the World Series. The games didn't start up again for ten days.

1. C; Sample answer: The earthquake was scary, so afraid is the best answer.

2. A; Sample answer: The article says that the stadium was damaged and bridges buckled, so they needed to be repaired. Also, the last paragraph says that the World Series didn't start up again for ten days, so game 3 was delayed. But I don't think people lost interest in baseball.

3. Sample answer: They were afraid of getting hurt or trapped and wanted to get away from the danger.

4. Sample answer: When the earth rumbles and moves, it can cause a lot of damage to buildings, streets, and bridges. People can get hurt.

Page 278

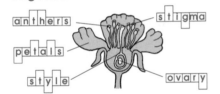

petals; stigma; anthers; ovary; style

Pages 279–283

Investigation 1: After 24 hours, Leaf 1 will be dry and Leaf 2 will be damp inside, but dry on the outside. Leaf 3, like some cactus leaves, will have minimum water loss because of its reduced surface area and waxy covering.

Investigation 2: Results will vary depending on materials used on the seed.

Page 284

rain; cloudy; frost; tornado; blizzard; lightning; sunshine; thunder

Pages 285–289

Investigation 1: Observations will vary depending on your location, time of year, and what kind of weather front is moving through your area.

Investigation 2: Tools will vary but should be based on a wind vane, anemometer, or a rain gauge.

Page 290

F	K	I	W	I	N	D	Y	A	C	S	O	O	S
A	I	S	G	S	M	R	O	L	G	U	N	S	H
I	S	T	O	R	M	Y	U	T	R	O	T	B	O
R	O	E	L	P	U	C	O	O	L	S	H	D	W
A	K	P	T	E	M	P	E	R	A	T	U	R	E
C	O	T	S	L	B	Y	H	O	T	R	N	M	R
L	E	L	I	N	M	S	B	R	T	U	D	J	S
O	C	V	B	F	X	U	H	E	S	T	E	A	D
U	L	B	F	B	T	N	Z	S	O	M	R	E	G
D	X	F	R	A	I	N	Y	R	Y	C	H	Z	H
Y	M	T	P	S	Q	Y	T	G	D	M	I	L	D

Sentences will vary but should each use a word from the Word Bank.

Pages 291–295

Investigation 1: A loud shout will vibrate the balloon skin, causing the cereal to "jump."

Investigation 2: Your child will probably see the rubber band vibrating and may hear a quiet sound (Step 2). Putting the rubber band around a cup and plucking it will make a much louder sound (Step 3). Placing a finger in the middle of the rubber band and plucking half of it will make a higher sound (Step 4). Moving one finger around while plucking with the other or stretching the rubber band (Step 5) will both change the pitch.

Pages 296–297

1. D; Sample answer: It says that the message will disappear. If something disappears, you can't see it.

2. A; Sample answer: The message you paint disappears, and then shows up again in brown. B, C, and D are true but are not surprising.

3. Sample answer: You let the paint dry until the message disappears.

4. Sample answer: You have to do them in a certain order. The numbers tell you that.

Pages 298–299

Most people know how the hiccups feel. Your body jumps inside. A "Hic!" sound pops out of your mouth. The hics repeat, making it hard to speak or be quiet. They can embarrass you.

What is the cause of hiccups? It has to do with a muscle inside your body called the **diaphragm** (DIE-uh-fram). The diaphragm looks like a rounded dome. It stretches across your chest to help you breathe.

The diaphragm usually works well. It keeps air flowing smoothly in and out of your body. But the diaphragm sometimes gets stuck or irritated and can't work well. It twitches, which interrupts the flow of air. The effect is the hiccups.

Luckily, hiccups are not serious. They usually go away on their own in a short time.

1. B; Sample answer: It's the only answer that the article talks about.

2. A; Sample answer: The second sentence in paragraph 2 says that it is a muscle.

3. Sample answer: It says in paragraph 3 that it helps keep air flowing smoothly in and out as you breathe.

4. Sample answer: I think that since hiccups make it hard to speak or keep quiet, some people feel embarrassed. Others might stare or laugh at a person with hiccups.

Page 300

Check your child's work.

ADDITION & SUBTRACTION

Page 302

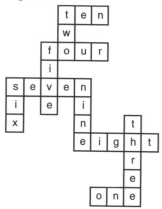

seven, nine

Page 303

Check that the your child has drawn the correct number of petals on each flower. Bows with 4, 6, 8, and 10 should be colored yellow. Bows with 3, 5, 7, and 9 should be colored purple.

Page 304

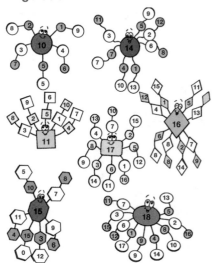

Page 305

A. 3, 2; B. 12, 5; C. 8, 6; D. 11, 7; E. 7, 5; F. 12, 3; G. 4, 1; H. 10, 8; I. 9, 4; J. 11, 5; Answers will vary.

Page 306

Beans talk

$4 + 2 = 6$; $7 + 7 = 14$; $9 + 5 = 14$;
$10 + 4 = 14$; $4 + 8 = 12$; $6 + 8 = 14$;
$11 + 3 = 14$; $14 + 0 = 14$; $7 + 2 = 9$;
$13 + 1 = 14$; $5 + 8 = 13$; $12 + 2 = 14$;
$7 + 4 = 11$; $5 + 9 = 14$

Page 307

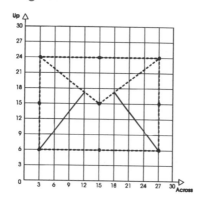

Page 308

21, 93, 78, 46, 44, 78; PLEASE
50, 67, 46, 79, 83, 59, 25, 66; THANK YOU
59, 25, 66, 32, 78; YOU'RE
80, 78, 93, 18, 25, 35, 78; WELCOME

Page 309

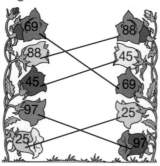

Answers will vary.

Page 310

38, 26, 97, 58, 67, 76, 79; 46, 84, 46, 89, 58, 48, 97; 58, 55, 65, 46, 40; THREE-FOURTHS, PACIFIC

Page 311

75, 23, 98, 86, 47, 34, 75, 99, AMERICAN; 86, 98, 33, 78, 64, 87, 32, 47, 78, 99, REVOLUTION; 64, 47, 51, 98, 86, 32, 21, LIBERTY; 51, 98, 64, 64, BELL

Page 312

1. $7 - 1 = 6$; 2. $9 - 2 = 7$;
3. $3 - 2 = 1$; 4. $8 - 4 = 4$;
5. $5 - 5 = 0$; 6. $6 - 1 = 5$;
7. $8 - 2 = 6$
The phone number is 671-4056.

Page 313

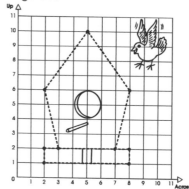

Page 314

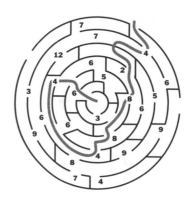

Page 315

A bat

$5 - 2 = 3$; $7 - 7 = 0$; $18 - 9 = 9$;
$17 - 3 = 14$; $15 - 4 = 11$; $18 - 4 = 14$;
$12 - 3 = 9$; $11 - 9 = 2$; $16 - 9 = 7$;
$7 - 4 = 3$; $10 - 8 = 2$; $15 - 7 = 8$;
$9 - 2 = 7$; $13 - 2 = 11$; $12 - 2 = 10$;
$15 - 2 = 13$; $9 - 6 = 3$; $6 - 6 = 0$;
$9 - 7 = 2$; $15 - 9 = 6$; $16 - 8 = 8$;
$9 - 5 = 4$; $9 - 1 = 8$

Page 316

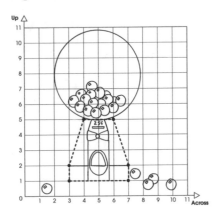

Page 317

68 − 26 = 42; 34 − 11 = 23;
91 − 20 = 71; 47 − 15 = 32;
67 − 13 = 54; 88 − 54 = 34;
19 − 12 = 7; 33 − 21 = 12;
69 − 59 = 10; 88 − 12 = 76;
28 − 24 = 4; 17 − 6 = 11;
57 − 55 = 2; 27 − 5 = 22;
97 − 13 = 84; 35 − 11 = 24;
81 − 21 = 60; 39 − 15 = 24;
60 − 10 = 50

Page 318

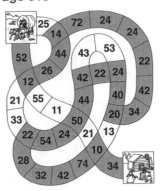

Page 319

62, 33, 23; 30, 21, 14; 61, 22, 41;
The bird with the difference of 30
should be colored red. The bird
with the difference of 14 should be
colored blue. The birds with the
differences of 22 and 33 should
be colored green.

Page 320

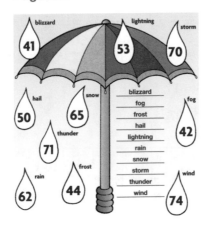

Page 321

54, 85, 43, 85; 43, 54, 67; 43, 67, 32;
32; Check your child's coloring.

Page 322

10, 12, 16; 18, 14, 19; 15, 11, 17;
Bowls with 11, 15, and 18 should
be colored yellow. Bowls with 10,
14, and 17 should be colored pink.
Bowls with 12, 16, and 19 should
be colored brown.

Page 323

Page 324

2 + 8 = 10; 24 + 7 = 31; 32 + 9 = 41;
1 + 9 = 10; 7 + 4 = 11; 45 + 5 = 50;
31 + 4 = 35; 11 + 9 = 20; 17 + 9 =
26; 22 + 13 = 35; 26 + 6 = 32; 19 + 9
= 28; 11 + 7 = 18; 16 + 22 = 38; 31 +
11 = 42; 14 + 9 = 23; 12 + 7 = 19;
40 + 14 = 54; 27 + 6 = 33; 12 + 9 =
21; 4 + 8 = 12; 41 + 21 = 62; 37 + 31
= 68; 16 + 6 = 22; 16 + 5 = 21; 10 +
24 = 34; 20 + 21 = 41; 15 + 5 = 20
Extra: Answers will vary.

Page 325

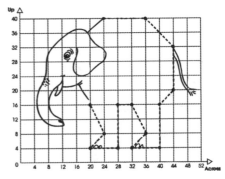

Page 326

A. 52, 93, 72, 93; B. 41, 62, 37, 37;
C. 23, 50, 62, 62; D. 60, 32, 81, 60;
E. 90, 44, 76, 44

Page 327

	71	93	90	52
92	90	91	86	92
81	81	73	42	92
85	74	92	90	94
51	41	93	81	

Page 328

Beach: Route #1—13 + 48 + 32 + 54
= 147 miles; Route #2—13 + 48 + 88
+ 39 = 188 miles
Mountains: Route #1—13 + 17 + 31 +
49 = 110 miles; Route #2—13 + 28 +
10 + 25 = 76 miles

Page 329

1. 21; 2. 26; 3. 14; 4. 31; 5. 35;
6. 28; 7. 27; 8. 29; 9. 58; 10. 33

Page 330

15 + 33 + 27 = 75; 27 + 23 + 12 = 62;
34 + 23 + 24 = 81; 15 + 25 + 10 = 50;
16 + 14 + 14 = 44; 12 + 31 + 17 = 60;
28 + 22 + 45 = 95; 43 + 27 + 27 = 97;
10 + 17 + 18 = 45; 29 + 13 + 16 = 58;
37 + 31 + 17 = 85; 51 + 23 + 17 = 91

Page 331

35: 3 tens 5 ones, 2 tens 15 ones;
47: 4 tens 7 ones, 3 tens 17 ones;
82: 8 tens 2 ones, 7 tens 12 ones;
94: 9 tens 4 ones, 8 tens 14 ones;
61: 6 tens 1 one, 5 tens 11 ones;
90: 9 tens 0 ones, 8 tens 10 ones

Page 332

A. (48) 89; B. 79, (46); C. 36, (76) D. (77)
59; E. (48) 14; F. 61, (68) G. 14, (39)
Answers will vary.

Page 333

A. 19, 39, 37; 1, 3, 2; B. 8, 6, 9; 2, 1,
3; C. 28, 37, 14; 2, 3, 1; D. 29, 38, 37;
1, 3, 2; E. 29, 36, 48; 1, 2, 3;
F. 18, 15, 19; 2, 1, 3

Page 334

35 – 17 = 18; 62 – 28 = 34;
53 – 14 = 39; 92 – 27 = 65;
82 – 23 = 59; 83 – 28 = 55;
67 – 48 = 19; 58 – 29 = 29;
72 – 17 = 55; 73 – 58 = 15;
42 – 26 = 16; 90 – 81 = 9;
52 – 28 = 24; 56 – 19 = 37

Page 335

45 – 39 = 6; 84 – 59 = 25;
72 – 55 = 17; 71 – 19 = 52;
84 – 25 = 59; 60 – 18 = 42;
98 – 29 = 69; 74 – 15 = 59;
71 – 17 = 54; 88 – 29 = 59;
82 – 68 = 14; 91 – 32 = 59;
34 – 16 = 18; 92 – 13 = 79;
43 – 35 = 8; 57 – 28 = 29
She had 15 tickets left.

Page 336

65 – 27 = 38, 38 + 27 = 65;
77 – 38 = 39, 39 + 38 = 77;
24 – 15 = 9, 9 + 15 = 24;
32 – 13 = 19, 19 + 13 = 32;
83 – 49 = 34, 34 + 49 = 83;
50 – 19 = 31, 31 + 19 = 50;
46 – 29 = 17, 17 + 29 = 46;
62 – 15 = 47, 47 + 15 = 62
Answers will vary.

Page 337

U. 81; L. 5; N. 60; C. 46; O. 90; P. 38;
H. 23; K. 63; S. 48; A. 14; G. 18;
M. 71; R. 69; KANGAROO; KOALA;
OPOSSUM; POUCH

Page 338

Check that your child has colored
the appropriate spaces. A. 21; B. 9;
C. 26; D. 8; E. 13; F. 17; G. 30; H. 7

Page 339

A. 28 + 25 = 53; B. 25 – 9 = 16;
C. 28 – 13 = 15; D. 12 + 9 = 21;
E. 12 – 9 = 3; F. 13 + 28 = 41;
G. 9 + 25 + 12 = 46; 98 students

Page 340

saw: 34 + 27 + 5 = 66; wrench:
48 + 36 + 15 = 99; hammer: 43 + 15
+ 27 = 85; pliers: 39 + 34 + 15 = 88;
A. 27 + 15 = 42; B. 34 – 5 = 29, 48 –
15 = 33, 43 – 15 = 28; 39 – 15 = 24;
43 + 15 + 27 + 5 + 34 + 39 + 48 + 15
+ 36 = 262

Page 341

A. 596, red; B. 995, blue; C. 877,
blue; D. 569, blue; E. 662, red;
F. 978, red; G. 968, red; H. 596, red;
I. 899, blue; J. 497, blue

Page 342

2 hundreds 7 tens,
8 hundreds 4 tens,
9 hundreds 3 tens,
7 hundreds 1 ten;
5 hundreds 6 tens,
3 hundreds 2 tens,
4 hundreds 9 tens,
6 hundreds 5 tens; 570; 804

Page 343

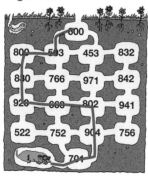

Page 344

207 + 545 = 752; 126 + 89 = 215;
328 + 347 = 675; 257 + 458 = 715;
547 + 129 = 676; 624 + 127 = 751;
108 + 107 = 215; 229 + 418 = 647;
258 + 268 = 526; 389 + 336 = 725;
417 + 129 = 546; 253 + 494 = 747

Page 345

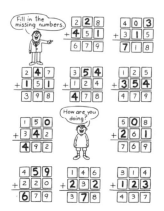

Page 346

A. $1.49 + $.50 + $.75 + $1.22 =
$3.96; B. $1.72 + $.65 + $1.17 =
$3.54; C. $1.86 + $1.84 + $.84 +
$1.07 = $5.61; D. $1.53 + $1.90 +
$1.22 + $.84 = $5.49; E. $1.86 +
$.50 + $1.17 = $3.53; F. $1.49 +
$.86 + $.75 = $3.10

Page 347

A. 123 + 406 + 406 = 935, orange;
B. 209 + 81 + 147 + 181 + 72 = 690,
green; C. 146 + 266 + 120 + 139 +
82 = 753, purple; D. 180 + 169 +
308 + 122 = 779, yellow; E. 154 +
154 + 188 + 93 + 82 + 170 = 841,
red; F. 107 + 173 + 38 + 280 + 38 +
54 + 78 = 768, blue

Page 348

40 tens, 20 tens, 70 tens, 50 tens;
10 tens, 90 tens, 80 tens, 30 tens

Page 349

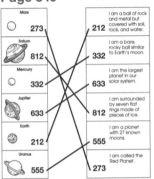

Page 350

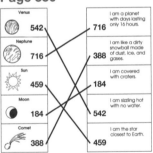

900, 800, 700, 600, 500, 400, 300,
200, 100, Subtract 100.; 900, 700,
500, 300, 100, Subtract 200.; 800,
600, 400, 200, Subtract 200.

Page 351

Page 352

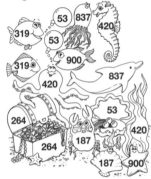

Check coloring.

Page 353

Page 354

A. 700 – 523 = 177; B. 300 – 156 =
144; C. 248 + 176 = 424, 600 – 424
= 176; D. 189 + 96 = 285, 400 – 285
= 115; E. 398 + 275 = 673, 900 – 673
= 227

Page 355

A. 168 – 159 = 9; B. 427 + 289 =
716; C. 507 – 278 = 229; D. 319 +
299 = 618; E. 826 – 697 = 129;
F. 258 + 273 = 531

Page 356

T. 500; O. 903; L. 285; P. 846;
A. 535; W. 951; I. 870; P. 528;
L. 979; I. 207; R. 821; I. 564;
O. 254; A. 853; N. 273; N. 869;
R. 517; H. 811; A. 894;
LION, TAPIR, PIRANHA, OWL

Page 357

B. 773; E. 569; L. 467; H. 374;
F. 248; D. 385; A. 796; N. 288;
I. 834; O. 883; M. 689; C.9; T. 896;
R. 800; P. 704;
FIREMAN, TEACHER, DOCTOR,
LIBRARIAN, POLICEMAN

Page 358

sandals $2.10 + swimsuits $6.89 +
sand toys $1.23 + swim ring
$1.46 = $11.68
mittens $.77 + coat $7.14 + hat
$1.23 + skis $3.74 = $12.88
$12.88 – $11.68 = $1.20

Page 359

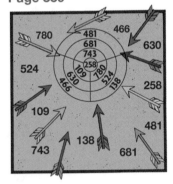

Answers will vary.

Page 360

427 + 282 = 709, 636 – 550 = 86;
963 – 189 = 774, 148 + 370 = 518,
550 + 370 = 920, 804 – 636 = 168;
189 + 751 = 940, 579 – 282 = 297,
963 – 148 = 815, 415 + 189 = 604

Page 361

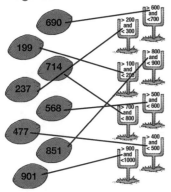

Page 362
Game 1: 637, 616; 353, 454; 851, 800; 189, 326; 554, 820
Game 2: 283, 218; 412, 417; 536, 509; 844, 873; 172, 128

MATH
Page 364

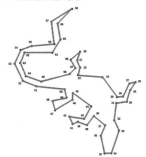

Page 365
A salamander

Page 366
1. 67; 2. 34, 35; 3. 42, 43; 4. 16, 18
5. 73, 74, 75; 6. 31, 32; 7. 10 12 14
16 8. 15 18 21 24; 9. 83, 84, 85, 86, 87, 88 10. after; 11. before; 12. after
13. before; 14. before; 15. before

Page 367
Your child should follow these numbers:
13, 7, 3, 9, 19, 23, 11, 5, 17, 67, 33, 25, 27, 35, 39, 37, 23, 57, 47, 43, 21, 15, 39, 29

Page 368
Top side of the street: 50, 52, 54, 56
Bottom side of the street: 51, 53, 55
Extra: The even numbers are on one side of the street. The odd numbers are on the other side of the street.

Page 369
1. the 1st   2. the 16th   3. James Buchanan   4. Andrew Johnson   5. 14

Page 370
1. 11 < 21; 2. 56 < 72; 3. 47 = 47;
4. 64 >10 5. 59 = 59; 6. 38 >17;
7. 526 < 527; 8. 159 > 42 9–16.
Answers will vary. 17. 73 61 54 37;
18. 96 43 24 22; 19. 79 78 69 51;
20. 51 37 27 15

Page 371
A sidewalk.   518, 315, 276, 693, 137, 564, 909, 811, 209, 717, 836, 321, 488, 857, 432, 707

4	3	2	1	9	9	5
B	A	R	K	S	I	G
8	1	7	1	7	5	6
R	M	Y	S	O	D	T
8	5	1	8	9	1	4
D	W	E	T	E	S	S
1	6	2	5	3	3	9
W	P	C	X	A	Z	P
4	9	7	7	0	7	0
L	J	F	S	R	M	L
8	3	6	9	2	0	9
H	F	Y	K	T	E	Q

Page 372

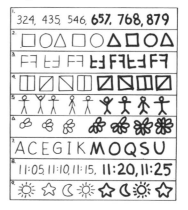
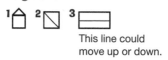

Page 373

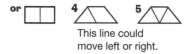
This line could move up or down.

This line could move left or right.

Page 374
1. 32, 42, 52, 62, 72, 82, 92; 2. 70, 60, 50, 40, 30, 20, 10; 3. 67, 57, 47, 37, 27, 17, 7; 4. 44, 55, 66, 77, 88, 99

Page 375
Answers will vary.

Page 376
A. 1F, 2G, 3B, 4C or A, 5E, 6I, 7E, 8H, 9G, 10G, 11C   B. 1B, 2F, 3D, 4I, 5F, 6E, 7A, 8D, 9I, 10F, 11I   C. 1H, 2C, 3C, 4G, 5G, 6C, 7F, 8I, 9B, 10C or A, 11F

Page 377
1. 5; 2. 8; 3. 11; 4. 26; 5. 6 6. 10;
7. 12; 8. 16; 9. 18; 10. 24
What did the rocket say when it left the party? "Time to take off."

Page 378
1. 15; 2. 6; 3. 24; 4. 12; 5. 27
6. 18; 7. 30; 8. 36; 9. 33; 10. 0
What did the owl say when someone knocked on its door? "Whoooo is it?"

Page 379

2 inches; 4 inches
Two possible answers: 6 inches, because it grew 2 inches each week; or 8 inches, because it doubled in height each week

Page 380

10, 10, 10 Extra: 2

Page 381

3 groups: fish, shells, animals with multiple legs/arms

Page 382

Answers will vary.

Page 383

1. 4 + 5 = 9; 2. 11 − 6 = 5;
3. 9 + 7 = 16; 4. 4 + 8 = 12;
5. 3 − 2 = 1; 6. 7 + 7 = 14;
7. 15 − 10 = 5; 8. 2 + 8 = 10;
9. 5 − 2 = 3

Page 384

15; 8

Page 385

Extra: Answers will vary.
Possible: Pepperoni is the most popular topping. Cheese is the next favorite topping. Sausage is the least favorite topping.

Page 386

1. 7:35, 25 minutes to 8
2. 9:15, 15 minutes after 9
3. 9:55, 5 minutes to 10
4. 3:50, 10 minutes to 4
5. 6:25, 25 minutes after 6
6. 2:05, 5 minutes after 2

Page 387

Alex's coins: 25¢ + 25¢ + 10¢ = 60¢
Billy's coins: 10¢ + 10¢ + 10¢ + 10¢ + 10¢ + 5¢ + 5¢ + 1¢ + 1¢ + 1¢ = 63¢
63¢ > 60¢ Billy has more money.

Pages 388–389

1. Teeny Sandwiches; 75¢
2. Donut Hole; 25¢   3. Peanuts
4. Gulp of Juice   5. 95¢   6. 50¢

Page 390

1. feet; 2. yards; 3. miles; 4. inches;
5. inches; 6. inches; 7. yards;
8. miles; 9. feet; 10. inches;
11. feet; 12. feet; 13. miles;
14. inches; 15. feet

Page 391

Sunny days: 12; Cloudy days: 8;
Rainy days: 5; Snowy days: 6

Page 392

1 + 1 + 1 = 3 inches;
2 + 2 + 2 = 6 inches;
4 + 4 + 4 = 12 inches

Page 393

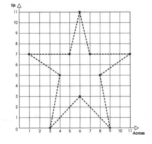

Page 394

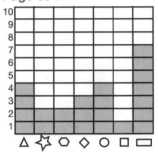

Page 395

Answers will vary.

Page 396

2, size; Correct pies: 1, 3, 5

Page 397

1. 1/2; 2. 1/8; 3. 1/4; 4. 1/4;
5. 1/2; 6. 1/67. 1/2; 8. 1/2;
9. 3/4; 10. 1/4; 11. 1/2

Page 398

2/2 matches triangle, 2/3 matches circle, 2/12 matches rectangle; color 1/2 circle, color the whole rectangle

Page 399

1/5 of the circle, 4/5 of the rectangle, 3 ants, 2 spiders,
0 bees, 5 worms

Page 400

2/10, 6/10, 2/10, 6/10, 7/10